Apprentice's Companion
for
LIFE SCIENCE

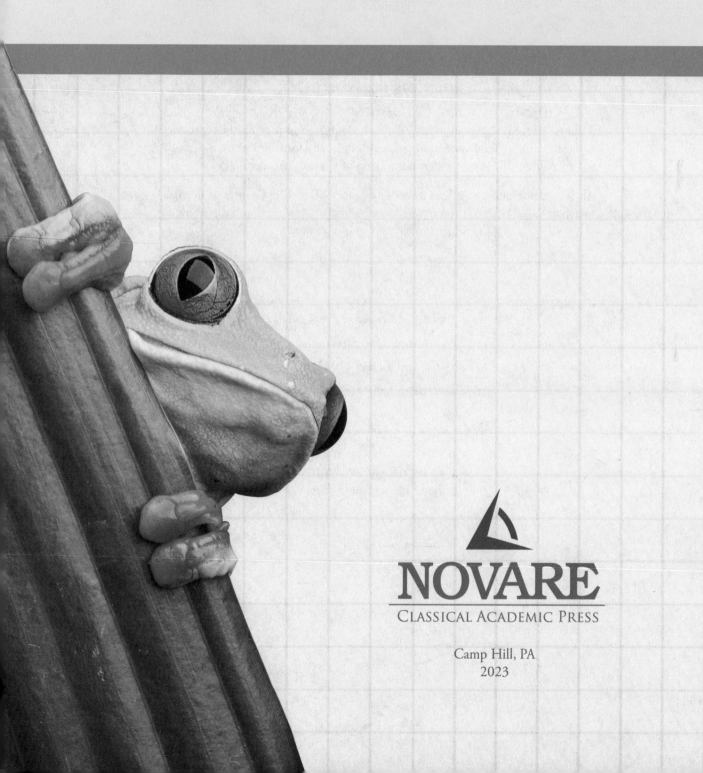

NOVARE
CLASSICAL ACADEMIC PRESS

Camp Hill, PA
2023

The Apprentice's Companion for Life Science
© Classical Academic Press®, 2023
Edition 1.0

ISBN: 978-1-60051-474-6

Classical Academic Press

515 S. 32nd Street

Camp Hill, PA 17011

www.ClassicalAcademicPress.com/Novare/

Cover design: Bill Wiist
Book Design: Bill Wiist

BB.01.23

Contents

The
Apprentice's Companion
for
LIFE SCIENCE

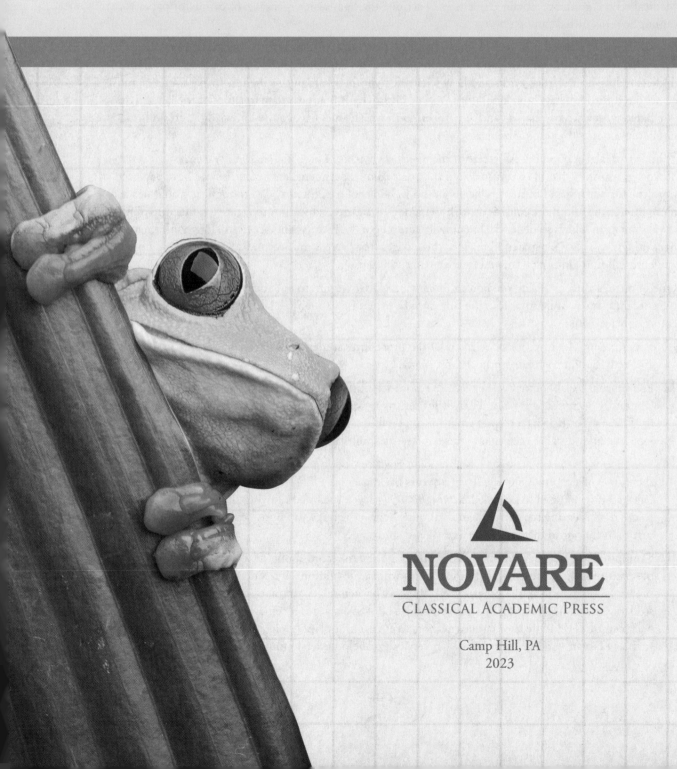

NOVARE
CLASSICAL ACADEMIC PRESS

Camp Hill, PA
2023

Introduction

Some things cannot be learned easily—or at all—from books. This is what apprenticeships are for—to provide learners a context in which skills and knowledge are acquired by direct modeling, mentoring, and practicing. Everyone knows about the apprenticeships that were part of the system of guilds back in the Middle Ages. Some of the terminology from those times survives in the trades today. Plumbers and electricians are rated in terms of Apprentice, Journeyman, and Master. But today, even some professional careers include apprenticeships: attorneys obtain clerkships to gain the experience needed to become judges. Medical school graduates obtain residencies to acquire the hands-on experience of caring for patients that cannot be transmitted through books.

In a similar way, science classes can convey the principles, concepts, and mathematical models associated with scientific inquiry and scientific theories. But laboratory skills, which are so important for understanding how science works and how scientific hypotheses are put to the test in experiments, must be acquired through hands-on laboratory work. This is why it is appropriate to think of the lab activities associated with a science class as an apprenticeship in which students acquire knowledge and skills that are not easily acquired by reading books.

Thinking of labs as apprenticeship one of the reasons why this book is called *The Apprentice's Companion*. The other reason is that in conceptualizing this manual of experiments and activities, we have departed from the formatting and content typically found in books of experiments. We thought it would be more interesting and more consistent with the tenets of classical education to create a multi-disciplinary environment in which students could enjoy literature, poetry, history, and art right along with their science. Accordingly, we have integrated items into these pages from across the arts and sciences that we hope students will find amusing, fun, and intellectually stimulating.

One of our reasons for calling the book a *companion* is that we aim to enhance the value of the book for the student. This volume combines the functions of experiments manual, lab journal, sketchbook, and commonplace book:

- Experiments Manual. This book includes the procedures students need for conducting 26 experiments and activities during their study of *Life Science*.

- Lab Journal. A lab journal is the place to record scientific observations and data collected during laboratory exercises. It can also be used for setting up graphs of data that can reveal underlying patterns in the data that help us interpret what the data tell us about how nature works. Students won't need a separate lab journal to accompany this course—it's built right into this book.

- Sketchbook. A sketchbook is a place to draw, practice drawing, and refine one's drawing. As depicted in the movie *Master and Commander* a few years back, there is a long tradition in which *naturalists*—those engaged in what used to be called *natural history*—develop refined drawing skills and put those skills to use documenting the natural world around them—the bugs and buds, leaves and leeches, trees and turtles in the world that we can marvel at and study.

- Commonplace Book. A commonplace book is a place to record thoughts, discoveries, questions, observations, quotes, events, mysteries, conundrums, meditations, references, words, witticisms, riddles, prayers, queries, and all the other strands that weave themselves around in an active and developing student's mind. The keeping of a commonplace book is a tradition central to classical education, dating back centuries. Hundreds of famous authors kept commonplace books, trained to do so at institutions such as Harvard College and Oxford University. For help understanding what a commonplace book is all about, check out the YouTube video by Jordan Clark entitled "you should start a commonplace book." At the end of that video, Jordan shares this quote from Jonathan Swift:

> A commonplace book is what a provident poet cannot subsist without, for this proverbial reason, that 'great wits have short memories' and, on the other hand, poets, being liars by profession, ought to have good memories; to reconcile these, a book of this sort is in the nature of a supplemental memory, or a record of what occurs remarkable in every day's reading or conversation. There you enter not only your own original thoughts, (which, a hundred to one, are few and insignificant) but such of other men as you think fit to make your own, by entering them there.

Supporting Text

The Apprentice's Companion for Life Science is designed to accompany *Life Science*, by Tracy Creek, published by Novare Science and Classical Academic Press (2023).

Teacher Notes

To accompany *The Apprentice's Companion for Life Science*, Classical Academic Press has available a downloadable PDF of Teacher Notes. The Teacher Notes PDF is available online for purchasers of this book at the My Library page of the purchaser's online account at Classical Academic Press (classicalsubjects.com). The Teacher Notes contains information about preparing solutions, time requirements, supply substitutions, and other items. It also contains photos obtained during our pilot runs of some of the experiments so that instructors unfamiliar with these experiments will know what to expect.

Several of the activities in this book call for students to use printed handouts for cutting out shapes. The PDFs of these handouts are also located among the documents in the purchaser's My Library account.

Materials and Equipment

The purchaser's My Library account mentioned above also contains a spreadsheet itemizing all materials required for these laboratory activities, as well as costs and suggested suppliers. To make acquiring supplies as convenient as possible, online supplier Home Science Tools (homesciencetools.com) has a kit of supplies designed to support this book.

On Natural History, Observation, and Sketching

Modern biological study grew out of the classical tradition of Natural History, which goes all the way back to Aristotle. Eighteenth- and nineteenth-century literature is full of references to natural historians and their work. Natural historians observed nature deeply, made careful and accurate sketches of organisms, collected and preserved specimens, and identified species (or named newly discovered ones). During the activities in this manual, you will do all these things and more.

But we want to encourage you to go beyond the activities described here and consider becoming a natural historian yourself. Observing nature is fun, relaxing, and rewarding. There is no end to the fascination one can experience by watching birds, lizards, insects, and other animals. In the past, many writers could readily identify all the native plants, birds, and other animals in their area. You can make it a project of your own to learn the names of the plant species where you live. Just think how much fun it would be to one of the few people walking around in your neighborhood who knew all the names of the plants! It's not hard, and a smartphone app such as NatureID makes easy work of identifying plants. The Merlin Bird ID app from Cornell University is the perfect tool for identifying birds.

Making sketches is also great fun, especially if you take the time to learn how to make accurate, beautiful drawings. The only real requirement is something to draw and lots of practice. Sketchbooks are available at most bookstores, and making sketches of plants, trees, birds, land animals, and grasses is relaxing and rewarding.

Finally, there are natural trails everywhere, and you can combine an interest in natural history with a hobby of going on nature hikes. Take your sketchbook, a pair of binoculars, a smartphone with the apps you need, and maybe even some collecting equipment (bags, containers, net, etc.) if you are interested in collecting, mounting, and displaying specimens.

We hope that as you go through the activities in this manual, the old spark of the natural historian will be ignited in you!

— Commonplace Space —

Students, as you begin this course of study, take time to pause and reflect. Embrace this educational experience as your own journey. What might you gain? What questions do you have going in that you would like to find answers for? What stories have you heard about the study of life science that inform your own goals? In what ways can this study help you to grow at this particular time in your life? Take time to reflect on these things as you enter this new course of study, and write down your thoughts!

Activity 1

Experiments and the Scientific Method

Factors Affecting Seed Sprouting

Today's Date _____

General Information

Life Science text reference: Chapter 1, Sections 1.3, 1.4

Estimated Time: 50 minutes to set up experiment; 5 minutes observation and note taking daily

Objectives

- Practice applying the Scientific Method.
- Form a testable hypothesis and design an experiment.
- Make conclusions based on data you collect.

Skills

- Sketching observations
- Labeling tables

Introduction

Chapter 1 of *Life Science* describes the Cycle of Scientific Enterprise, and how the "scientific method" applies to conducting scientific experiments. In this activity, you put the steps of the scientific method into practice as you investigate one factor that might affect the sprouting of seeds.

A new gardener who wants to plant a row of green beans and a row of corn might consult the back of the seed package to learn how deep to plant the seeds in the soil, how far apart the seeds should be planted, and how often they should be watered. In order to sprout, seeds must have moisture and warmth. Your task is to investigate whether seeds sprout better in darkness or in light.

Materials (per student)

- dried beans (6)
- popcorn kernels (6)
- paper towels (8)
- black construction paper (2 pieces)
- small Ziploc bags (4)
- water
- tape
- small centimeter ruler

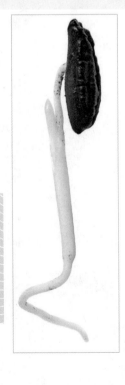

Though I do not believe a plant will spring up where no seed has been, I have great faith in a seed. Convince me that you have a seed there, and I am prepared to expect wonders.

—Henry David Thoreau, from *The Dispersion of Seeds*

Procedure

Hypothesis

1. Form a hypothesis that predicts whether seeds sprout better in darkness or in light. Write your hypothesis as an if-then statement, as represented by these examples:

    • If the coffee is especially sweet, then more children will want to drink it.

    • If the snowpack is not thick enough by spring, then the valley will have little water this summer.

Our Hypothesis

_____

_____

_____

Testing Method

2. Determine how you will test your hypothesis by designing an experiment using the materials provided. Some things to consider include how you will manipulate the variable you are testing (darkness or light), how your procedure will incorporate multiple trials, how you will keep all other conditions constant, what each member of your team will be doing, and how you will collect and record data from your experiment.

3. Write your experimental procedure in the space below. List the measurements you will make, the conditions you will control, and the data you will collect. Write your experimental design clearly so that another team could read it and repeat the experiment as you plan to do it.

Our Experimental Procedure

_____

_____

_____

_____

_____

_____

_____

_____

_____

_____

_____

_____

_____

_____

Conduct Your Experiment and Collect Data

4. Following the procedure you designed, conduct your experiment. Use the space below to sketch your observations. Label your sketches with the date and time of your observations.

5. Create data tables in the grid area below. Label the trial number, the variable you are testing and measuring in each trial, and the values of the measurements (with units of measure).

6. As you conduct your experiment, collect data and record them in the data area.

Sketches

— Experimental Data —

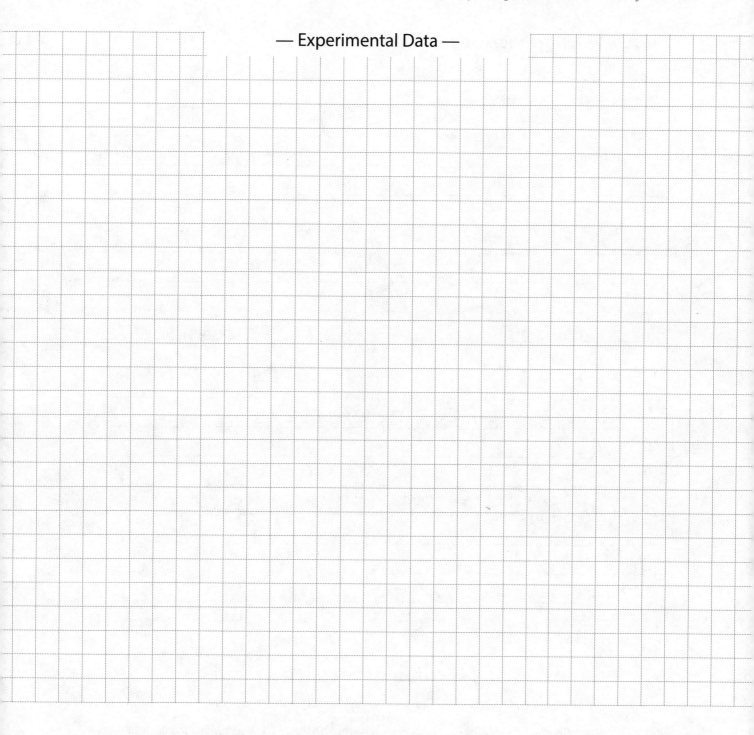

7. After you have completed collecting data, use this section to describe your data and to consider how they relate to your hypothesis. Include these ideas:

• What variable did you manipulate to determine its effect on seed sprouting?

• What did you find? How do the data show this?

• Were you surprised by what you found?

8. Explain whether your hypothesis was confirmed, spell out what you learned, and judge whether your results were definitive or inconclusive.

Our Analysis, Discussion, and Conclusion

_____

_____

_____

_____

_____

_____

_____

_____

_____

_____

_____

_____

_____

_____

_____

_____

_____

_____

What is commonly called a weed

What is commonly called a weed
has pushed, wriggled and writhed
through a fissure in the concrete pavement,
seeking sunshine, photosynthesis, survival.
The tendril is weak, fragile, vulnerable,
its very being tenuous but, that stem
extruding from where its seed was blown,

accidently washed or lodged,
proclaims nature will one day reclaim its own.
Its roots will create cracks that, in turn,
will receive other migrant seeds or spores.
Organisms that will grow and expand,
crumbling the concrete around it into sand.

—Jeremy Gadd

Exercises

1. Use the table below to describe how your experiment followed the steps of the scientific method. Refer to Table 1.1 in Chapter 1 of *Life Science* for an example of a table like this.

Step	Task	Remarks
1	State the problem.	
2	Research the problem.	
3	Form a hypothesis.	
4	Conduct an experiment.	
5	Collect data.	
6	Analyze the data.	
7	Form a conclusion.	
8	Repeat the work.	

2. Write a theory statement that explains the need for light in sprouting seeds.

_____

_____

Activity 2

Truth vs. Scientific Facts

Today's Date _____

General Information

Life Science text reference: Chapter 1, Sections 1.5, 1.6

Estimated Time: 10 minutes

Objectives

? Practice classifying truth statements.
? Practice identifying scientific facts.

Skills

? Distinguishing between scientific facts and truth claims

Introduction

Chapter 1 of *Life Science* describes the difference between scientific facts and theories. The chapter also describes three ways we can know truth. In this activity, you practice classifying truth statements and scientific facts.

Procedure

Truth vs. Scientific Facts

1. With a partner, discuss the ideas that you read about in Sections 1.5 and 1.6. Working together, come up with three truth statements based on direct observation and three scientific facts. Write your ideas in the table below.

Truth Statements	Scientific Facts
When I drop this rubber ball on the sidewalk, it bounces.	Onion root tips contain actively dividing cells.

2. Next, write a statement that describes the difference between a truth statement and a scientific fact.

_____

_____

Syllogisms

3. Invent your own syllogism. Label the lines below as the two premises and conclusion. Be sure the premises are true (as well as you can), and that the logic is valid.

_____

_____

_____

If you tell the truth, you don't have to remember anything.

— attributed to Mark Twain

— Commonplace Space —

Activity 3   Collecting, Preserving, and Mounting Specimens

Flowering Plants, Tree Leaves, and Insects

Today's Date _____

General Information

Your teacher may assign one or more of three collection activities. See the Appendix for more complete instructions.

Estimated Time: two or more hours outside of regular class

Introduction

Students of life science can find much value in the practice of collecting flowering plants, insects, or tree leaves. Collections help students develop skills in observation and classification. Many well-known scientists began to develop their interests and skills through collecting as children. Carl Linnaeus, the Swedish botanist known for developing a system for naming, ranking, and classifying organisms, showed great interest in plants when he was very young. William Smith, the English geologist who first mapped the strata of England, enjoyed collecting fossilized sea urchins and brachiopods as a schoolboy. Beloved children's book illustrator Beatrix Potter displayed a keen interest in natural history and devoted much time to drawing and painting fungi. Collections and sketches of flora and fauna have also been important in historical expeditions such as the voyages of Captain Cook and the Lewis and Clark expedition. Today, biologists refer to organized collections of dried plants (*herbariums*) to help them determine the range of certain species, that is, the region to which the species is native.

Objectives

- Become more aware of the plants and insects growing and living around you.
- Make connections between your local environment and our study of living things.
- Become familiar with taxonomy.

Materials (per group of 2)

- See the Appendix

Procedure

Review the Appendix and decide which of the three collecting projects you will complete. You may choose to complete more than one project if you desire. Keep in mind that collections of living organisms are easier to accomplish while the weather is warm. Record your choice below. Also, describe your general plan for completing this project, including the timeframe and some dates for completing major milestones.

_____

_____

_____

_____

_____

— Commonplace Space —

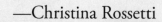

The lily has an air,
And the snowdrop a grace,
And the sweetpea a way,
*   And the heartsease a face,—*
Yet there's nothing like the rose
When she blows.

—Christina Rossetti

Activity 4 Elements and Compounds

Comparing Physical Properties

Today's Date _____

General Information

Life Science text reference: Chapter 2, Sections 2.1, 2.2

Estimated Time: 10 minutes

Introduction

The physical properties of a substance include color, density, state, appearance, and texture. Typically, the physical properties of a compound are quite different from the physical properties of the elements the compound is composed of. In this activity, you practice careful observation while comparing chemical elements with chemical compounds.

Objectives

◌ Describe how physical properties of elements change when elements combine chemically to form compounds.

Skills

◌ Careful observation of properties of matter
◌ Writing descriptions of observations

Materials (per group of 2)

Small jars (6), labeled, containing:

◌ sulfur (S)
◌ copper (Cu)
◌ copper(II) sulfate ($CuSO_4$)
◌ carbon (C)
◌ water (H_2O)
◌ table sugar (sucrose, $C_{12}H_{22}O_{11}$)

Procedure

1. Without opening them, carefully observe the contents of each small jar. Record as many physical properties as you can for each sample. (Since the actual densities are unknown, simply compare the relative densities as well as you can.)

_____

_____

_____

_____

_____

16

2. Compare the properties of the individual elements of each set with the compound formed from the elements. Record your observations.

_____

_____

_____

_____

The antiseptic properties of copper have been known since ancient times. Since brass is about two-thirds copper, one of the best things you can do to sanitize your house is simply to install brass doorknobs! In his book *The Disappearing Spoon*, journalist Sam Kean writes, "If certain bacteria, fungi, or algae inch across something made of copper, they absorb copper atoms, which disrupt their metabolism (human cells are unaffected). The microbes choke and die after a few hours. This effect—the oligodynamic, or 'self-sterilizing' effect—makes metals more sterile than wood or plastic and explains why we have brass doorknobs and metal railings in public places. It also explains why most of the well-handled coins of the U.S. realm contain close to 90 percent copper or (like pennies) are copper-coated."

In 2021, science.org reported that Native Americans living in the Wisconsin area were making arrowheads out of copper around 8,500 years ago—an arrowhead found there has been reliably dated to this age. The Wisconsin arrowhead is now one of the oldest known copper artifacts and the Native Americans who made it among the earliest known coppersmiths. This copper-working group of people is known as the Old Copper Culture.

The antique name for sulfur was *brimstone*. The phrase "fire and brimstone" refers to a fiery style of preaching about Hell and damnation and appears in several verses in the King James Version translation of the Bible. Passages where the phrase appears include Luke 17:29, Revelation 14:10, Revelation 20:10, and Revelation 21:8. The accompanying image is a woodcut by French artist Gustave Doré, of the flight of Lot, described in Genesis 19. Doré illustrated many biblical events in an extensive series of famous—and exquisite—woodcuts.

Activity 5

Organic Molecules

Identifying Healthy Foods

Today's Date _____

General Information

Life Science text reference: Chapter 2, Section 2.3

Estimated Time: 20 minutes

Introduction

In addition to carbohydrates, lipids, and proteins, nutrient-dense foods provide your body with necessary vitamins and minerals. A healthy diet includes food from all food groups: vegetables, fruits, grains, dairy, protein foods, and oils. Added sugars, saturated fat, or sodium should be avoided for the most part. The table to the right shows recommended daily amounts of food from each group for a teenager who requires about 2,000 calories per day.

Food Group	Daily Amount of Food
Vegetables	2 ½ cups
Fruits	2 cups
Grains	6 ounces
Dairy	3 cups
Protein Foods	5 ½ ounces
Oils	27 grams
Added Sugar	Less than 10% of total
Saturated Fat	Less than 10% of total
Sodium	1,800 mg

Objectives

Identify healthy foods that provide essential organic molecules.

Skills

Reading tables for information

Materials (per group of 2)

Food Images pdf file
scissors
glue stick

Procedure

Cut apart the food images and glue them into the columns below to create three meals for one day that meet the daily food requirements of a teenager without exceeding 2,000 calories or 1,800 mg of sodium. Refer to the nutrition table below on page 20 for guidance.

Breakfast	Lunch	Dinner

Nutrition Table				
Food	Food Calories (typical serving size)	Saturated Fat (g)	Sodium (mg)	Sugar (g)
milk (1%)	100	1.5	80	11
apple	95	0.1	1.8	19
apple Juice	35	0	15	8
baked potato	161	0.1	17	2
banana	105	0.1	1.2	14
bell peppers	32	0	2.3	2.9
black beans	227	0.2	1.7	0.6
black coffee	0	0	20	0
blueberries	57	0	1	10
breakfast burrito	310	7	800	2
broiled salmon	257	2.1	551	0.1
brown rice	109	0.2	1	0
butter	102	7.3	91	0
carrots	16	0	27	1.6
cheeseburger	300	6	720	7
chickpeas	269	0.4	11	7.9
Coke (12 oz can)	140	0	40	39
corn (1 ear)	99	0.2	1	4.7
egg breakfast sandwich	310	6	770	3
french fries	220	1.5	180	0
fruit yogurt	162	0.2	99	32
grape jelly (1 tbsp)	50	0	6.3	11
hotcakes	580	6	550	45
lean steak	196	4	74	0
macaroni and cheese	511	12	833	5.6
mixed greens	20	0.2	31	1.8
oatmeal	166	0.7	9.4	0.6
orange juice	150	0	35	32
peanut butter	188	3	152	2.1
peas	134	0.1	4.8	9.5
roast chicken	190	3.2	62	0
sour cream	24	1.2	3.7	0.4
tomatoes	22	0	6.2	3.2
water	0	0	0	0
whole grain bread	81	0.2	146 mg	1.4 g

— Commonplace Space —

Here is where you can write a poem singing the praises of your favorite food!
(Be sure to mention the nutrients it provides.)

Activity 6

Cell Organization and Function

Today's Date _____

General Information

Life Science text reference: Chapter 2, Section 2.4

Estimated Time: 30 minutes

Introduction

After studying Chapter 2 of *Life Science*, you are familiar with the organization of different types of cells. In this activity, you identify, color, and label the organelles in three types of cells—prokaryotic, eukaryotic plant, and eukaryotic animal.

Objectives

◢ Classify cells as prokaryotic or eukaryotic.
◢ Identify cell organelles.

Skills

◢ Careful observation of similarities and differences between similar structures

Materials (per group of 2)

◢ colored pencils

Procedure

Neatly color and label the organelles within each of the following cell sketches. Refer to your textbook as needed.

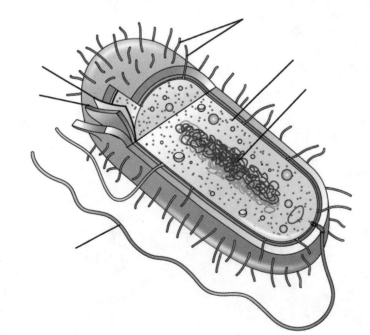

Prokaryotic cell

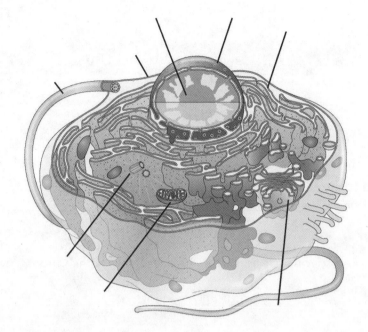

Eukaryotic animal cell

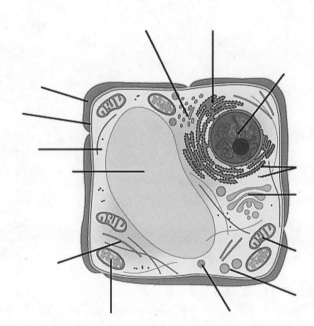

Eukaryotic plant cell

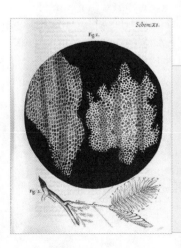

We owe our use of the term cell to Robert Hooke (1605–1703), an eminent British scientist. In 1665, Hooke published his book *Micrographia*, which details his extensive investigations with the microscope. The book is famous for Hooke's fantastically detailed sketches of objects observed through the microscope. *Micrographia* contains the original use of the term *cell* to describe the basic unit of life found in all organisms. Observing a thin slice of cork in the microscope, Hooke wrote: "I could exceeding plainly perceive it to be all perforated and porous, much like a Honey-comb…[the] walls (as I may so call them) or partitions of those pores were neer [sic] as thin in proportion to their pores, as those of thin films of Wax in a Honey-comb (which enclose and constitute the *sexangular cells*) are to theirs."

Activity 7

Observation and Classification

Today's Date _____

General Information

Life Science text reference: Chapter 3, Sections 3.2, 3.3, 3.4

Estimated Time: 10 minutes for initial observations; 5 hours for bone preparation; 30 minutes for sorting, classifying, and labeling bones

Introduction

In this activity, you observe muscle tissue and take a closer look at the skeletal system, using chicken as a specimen.

Objectives

- Compare muscle tissue types.
- Observe and classify bones.
- Observe the functioning of the skeletal system.

Skills

- Preparation of a biological specimen
- Identification of types of bones
- Observation of a system

Materials (per group of 2)

- whole chicken
- dish soap
- bleach
- gloves
- apron
- safety glasses
- stock pot
- tap water
- cook stove
- bucket with gallon mark
- measuring cup
- towel
- camera (or phone), computer, and printer
- glue stick

Procedure

1. **Examining Muscle Tissue.** Before you begin preparing your bones, take a few minutes to examine the different types of muscle tissue on the chicken's skeleton. The dark muscles on the wings, thighs, and drumsticks rely mostly on fat for fuel and contain proteins that convert fat into energy. The white muscles on the breast of the chicken rely mostly on glycogen (a type of sugar) for fuel. Examine the liver and heart if you have them. They represent two more types of muscle tissue: smooth (the liver) and cardiac (the heart). Notice the differences in color and texture. Wash your hands when you are done examining the muscle tissue.

2. **Preparing bones.** Place the whole chicken, including the neck if you have it, in a stock pot and cover it with tap water. Put the pot on the stove and turn the burner on high. Boil the chicken for 20 minutes. Using potholders, remove the pot from the stove. Let the chicken cool and then strip as much meat from the chicken's bones as possible. Return the bones to the pot, cover them with fresh water, and simmer them on the stove for 2 hours or more, until you can easily remove the rest of the muscle tissue (meat).

3. Place the bones in a bowl of warm soapy water and then rinse them clean with fresh tap water. Pour the used water down the drain.

4. While wearing latex gloves, eye protection, and an apron, prepare a solution of 1 gallon of water and 1 cup of bleach in a bucket. Soak the bones in the solution for 30 minutes. Pour the used water down the drain and rinse the bones in fresh tap water.

5. Spread the bones on a towel to dry.

6. **Classifying bones.** While referring to the illustrations of the axial skeleton and the appendicular skeleton in your textbook, sort your bones into two groups: axial and appendicular. Take a picture of the separated sets of bones, print it on regular copy paper, and glue it in the space below. Write a description of which bones you placed in each group.

Photo

Write a description of your two sets of bones here.

_____

_____

_____

_____

_____

_____

_____

7. Study the diagram below illustrating human bone types. Then classify your chicken bones as flat, short, irregular, or long. Sort them into these four groups. Take a picture of the four sets of bones, print it on regular copy paper, and glue it in the space below. Sketch one of each type of bone in the table proved on the next page.

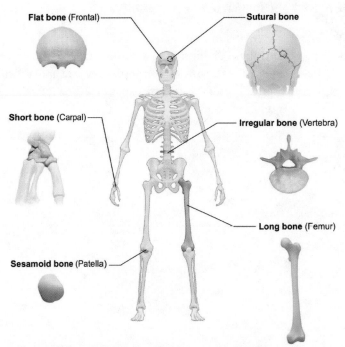

Classification of Bones by Shape

─ Photo ─

so much depends
upon

a red wheel
barrow

glazed with rain
water

beside the white
chickens

—William Carlos Williams

8. Sketch one of each type of bone in the following table.

Flat	Short
Irregular	**Long**

Activity 8

The Digestive System

Today's Date _____

General Information

Life Science text reference: Chapter 3, Sections 3.7, 3.8

Estimated Time: 15 minutes

Introduction

Scientists often make physical models to help them understand things in the natural world. In this activity, you make a physical model of the stomach from a plastic bag. Then you develop your own digesting machine on paper and diagram how it functions.

Objectives

- Model the mechanical digestion processes of the stomach.
- Diagram the path of the digestive tract.

Skills

- Translating written descriptions into diagrams
- Identifying the parts of the digestive system

Materials (per group of 2)

- resealable bag (1 gal)
- banana, soft and ripe
- soda crackers (3)
- tablespoon measure

- table knife
- water
- food coloring
- colored pencils

Procedure

1. Peel and slice the banana and crush the crackers. Place the banana pieces and crushed crackers into the plastic bag. Add three tablespoons of water and three or four drops of food coloring.

2. Flatten the bag to get most of the air out. Then seal the bag tightly.

3. Write what you observe happening in the bag:

   _____

   _____

4. Gently mash and squeeze the bag for 30–45 seconds. Examine the contents again. Write down your observations:

   _____

   _____

   _____

5. The plastic bag and its contents represent a model of a stomach digestion food. What do your hands represent in this model?

    _____

6. What do the water and food coloring represent in the model?

    _____

    _____

7. Explain how the churning motions in the stomach help with digestion.

    _____

    _____

8. In the space below, design a digesting machine of your own that models the digestive system. Refer to Section 3.7 in the text, and make sure your model performs all the functions of the digestive system. Then draw a flow chart (diagram) of your model with arrows showing the passage of food through each part of the system. Label the diagram to indicate the function of each part.

Sketches

> *I don't know a better preparation for life than love of poetry and a good digestion.*
>
> —Zona Gale, from *The Loves of Pelleas and Etarre*

Activity 9   Diffusion

Observing Flow through Semipermeable Membranes

Today's Date _____

General Information

Life Science text reference: Chapter 3, Section 3.8, and the feature entitled "Diffusion, Osmosis, and Hemodialysis"

Estimated Time: 30 minutes

Introduction

Chapter 3 of *Life Science* describes the excretory system. The central feature of excretory system is the two kidneys. Each kidney comprises about a million nephrons, and each nephron contains a glomerulus. The walls of the capillaries in the glomerulus function as semipermeable membranes. In this activity, you make a physical model to simulate the diffusion that takes place in the glomerulus.

Objectives

- Model the process of diffusion through a semipermeable membrane.
- Investigate the details of how kidneys function.

Skills

- Comparing models and real physical systems
- Identifying the parts of the excretory system

Materials (per group of 2)

- beaker, 600 mL or large (quart-sized or larger) glass jar (2)
- cornstarch
- iodine in dropper bottle
- tablespoon measure
- plastic spoon
- distilled water
- graduated cylinder, 100 mL, or measuring cup
- sealable plastic bags, small (2)

Background

Diffusion is the movement of molecules from an area of high concentration to an area of low concentration. In a cell, diffusion takes place through the cell membrane, which is semipermeable. This means that some molecules are small enough to pass through the membrane, while larger molecules cannot. In this experiment, the plastic bag represents a cell; the plastic itself is a semipermeable membrane representing the cell membrane. Cornstarch solution contains relatively large starch molecules; iodine solution contains much smaller iodine molecules. When iodine comes into contact with starch, the solution changes color.

Procedure

1. Put about 100 mL of distilled water into one of the plastic bags. Add several drops of iodine—enough to make the water very orange. Being careful not to spill the contents, seal the bag.

2. Add distilled water to one large beaker until it is half full. Add several drops of iodine—enough to make the water very orange.

3. Place one heaping tablespoon of cornstarch in the second plastic bag. Add about 100 mL of distilled water. Seal the bag and mix the contents until they appear milky.

4. Fill the second beaker about half full of distilled water. Add three or four heaping tablespoons of cornstarch and stir until the solution appears milky.

5. Below, you will place the bag containing the starch solution into the glass jar containing the iodine solution, and you will place the plastic bag containing the iodine solution into the glass jar containing the starch solution. In the space below, predict what will occur in each system (each set of jar and plastic bag).

Our Hypothesis

_____

_____

_____

6. Place the plastic bag containing the starch solution into the glass jar containing the iodine solution. Place the plastic bag containing the iodine solution into the glass jar containing the starch solution.

7. Observe the two systems for several minutes. In the space below, describe your observations and summarize the results of the experiment. Has diffusion occurred? Do the results support your hypothesis? Which system best represents the glomerulus of the kidney? Explain. Which solution best represents liquid waste or urine? Explain.

_____

_____

_____

_____

_____

_____

_____

_____

_____

The marvels of nature are everywhere. The beautiful ostrich egg, with its geometrically perfect form and its dimpled, glossy finish, is a wonder in itself. (The books in the picture indicate how large these eggs are.) But the egg's design is even more wonderful—Inside all amniotic eggshells, several semipermeable membranes (the chorion surrounding the embryo, as well as additional membranes on the inside of the eggshell) allow gas exchange through the wall of the egg. Thus, the growing embryo can breathe!

Activity 10

The Phases of the Cell Cycle

Today's Date _____

General Information

Life Science text reference: Chapter 4, Section 4.1

Estimated Time: 30 minutes

Introduction

The cell theory states that all living things are made of one or more cells and that all living cells arise from pre-existing cells by division. Mitosis, the process by which most cells multiply, is continuous. A cell moves from prophase through telophase in about two hours. The image at the right is from a slide of an onion root tip through a microscope. If you look closely, you can find cells in various stages of mitosis. In this activity, you make a model of the cell cycle.

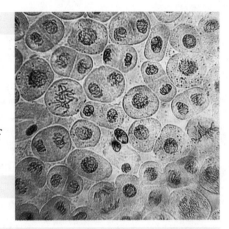

Objectives

✎ Describe each phase in the cell cycle.

Skills

✎ Designing a model
✎ Interpreting images

Materials (per group of 2–4)

✎ fine yarn or crewel embroidery thread (several colors)
✎ scissors

✎ glue stick
✎ card stock
✎ pen

Procedure

1. The stages of mitosis are described in *Life Science* Section 4.1 and Figure 4.2. Refer to these as needed.

2. Using the colored yearn and cardstock, create a model representing the five steps in the division of a cell nucleus with three pairs of chromosomes. (Human cells have 23 pairs of chromosomes, but a model with 46 chromosomes would be rather crowded!) Your model must include the five phases of the cell cycle: interphase, prophase, metaphase, anaphase, and telophase. Label your model. Include a brief description of each phase in the cell cycle.

Research

Research the number of chromosomes in the cells of some other organisms. Begin with fruit flies and then choose several other organisms. Record your findings in the table. Do you think the number of chromosomes gives some indication about how complex an organism is? Explain your answer.

Number of Chromosomes per Cell	
Species	**Number of Chromosomes**
humans	46
fruit flies	

— Commonplace Space —

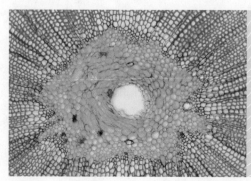

I'd heard that life was cellular, in the body and outside the body. Nobody'd ever put it in so many words, but I kept hearing something that made me see that life was cellular. (Even the Communists have cells.)

—Robert Frost

Activity 11

Vegetative Propagation

Today's Date _____

General Information

Life Science text reference: Chapter 4, Section 4.2

Estimated Time: 15 minutes, plus observation over several weeks

Introduction

Vegetative reproduction, or vegetative propagation, occurs when plants are grown from parts other than a seed. In this activity, you try take advantage of this process to grow fresh produce from kitchen scraps.

Objectives

- Observe plant reproduction.
- Recognize parts of plants that can reproduce.

Skills

- Growing plants
- Sketching

Materials (per class)

Groups of students can each tackle 2–3 different plants, with some plants being grown by more than one group. Alternatively, the class (or homeschool) can cooperate to start one of each kind.

- kitchen knife
- multiple bowls and pots for starting and planting
- potting soil
- celery stem (base of celery)
- herbs
- garlic cloves
- ginger
- green onions
- lettuce
- potatoes

Procedure

1. Examine the plant parts you will use for growing. Compare them with the pictures and information in Section 4.2.3 of *Life Science*. Identify whether you are growing plants from bulbs, corms, runners, rhizomes, or tubers. Sketch and label the plant parts you identify on the following page.

2. **Celery.** Cut about 2 inches from the base of a bunch of celery. Place the base in a shallow container of water. Wet the top daily, keeping it moist. Replace the water every couple of days. When a root system begins to grow, transplant the celery into a pot.

3. **Herbs.** Cut a branch of an herb at the node. Place the cut portion in a jar of water on a windowsill. Replace the water every couple of days. When roots emerge, transplant the herbs into a pot.

4. **Garlic.** Plant the cloves pointed side up in soil. Grown indoors, they will produce greens. Planted outdoors in the fall before the first frost and they will grow fresh garlic bulbs the following year.

5. **Ginger.** Soak the root in warm water overnight. Plant it horizontally (flat) in a container of soil. Place the pot in a sunny spot. Keep the soil moist. Harvest the ginger after several months.

6. **Green Onions.** Cut the green part of the onion off, leaving a small amount of pale green along with the white part. Place the onion in water a container of water on a sunny windowsill. Replace the water every couple of days. You can eat the green portions as they grow or transplant the onions into a pot of soil.

7. **Lettuce.** Cut the base off a head of lettuce. Place it in a bowl of water. Replace the water every couple of days. Use the fresh leaves as they grow.

8. **Potatoes.** Cut potatoes into 2-inch pieces and let them dry for a couple of days. Plant them in soil and water regularly.

Sketches

There are lots of interesting facts about some of the plants used in this activity. For example, the ginger "root" is not a root at all—it's a rhizome. Ginger has been cultivated for thousands of years for both its flavor enhancing properties as well as its many health benefits. And all this applies to garlic, too, except the rhizome bit. A cluster of garlic cloves is a bulb. And guess what? All this applies to onions as well. And like garlic, onions are bulbs. All three have been cultivated from ancient times. All three have numerous health benefits. All three add spectacular flavors to food. Oh, and one more thing—people love to write poems about them!

Activity 12

Investigating Single-Gene Human Traits

Today's Date _____

General Information

Life Science text reference: Chapter 4, Section 4.3

Estimated Time: 15 minutes

Introduction

Everyone has two biological parents and two sets of genes: one from the mother and one from the father. Although the two sets of genes pair up according to the traits they code for, any two genes in a pair might represent different alleles. For example, one allele in the pair might code for long fingers while the other codes for short fingers. While most human traits are the result of a combination of several genes, a few traits are determined by a single gene. Dominant traits are expressed when the individual has one or two copies of the dominant allele. Recessive traits are only expressed if the individual has two copies of the recessive allele.

Objectives

- Observe phenotypes produced by a single gene.
- Explain the idea of dominant gene inheritance.

Skills

- Writing gene combinations

Procedure

The chart on the next page lists dominant human traits that are coded for by a single gene. The dominant form of a gene is represented as an uppercase letter such as "E" for detached earlobes. The recessive form of a gene is represented by the same letter, lower-case, such as "e" for attached earlobes. Examine each trait and indicate whether you have the dominant form. If you do, write "Dominant" in the fourth column. If not, write "Recessive" in the fourth column. Write your possible gene combinations in the last column. For example, if you have detached earlobes, your possible gene combinations are EE and Ee.

— Commonplace Space —

Trait	Description	Do I have this trait?	Dominant or Recessive	Possible Gene Combination
Detached earlobes (E)	Earlobes hang free			
Curved little finger (F)	When hand is flat on a table, the little finger curves toward other fingers			
Left thumb on top (T)	When hands are clasped, the left thumb is on top			
Cleft chin (C)	The middle of the chin has a dimple or cleft			
Freckles (F)	Small patches of light brown color on skin			
Full lips (L)	Plump on both the top and bottom			

Heredity

I am the family face;
Flesh perishes, I live on,
Projecting trait and trace
Through time to times anon,
And leaping from place to place
Over oblivion.

The years-heired feature that can
In curve and voice and eye
Despise the human span
Of durance—that is I;
The eternal thing in man,
That heeds no call to die.

—Thomas Hardy

Activity 13

Enzymes

The Action of Biological Catalysts

Today's Date _____

General Information

Life Science text reference: Chapter 5, Section 5.2.1

Estimated Time: 10 minutes

Introduction

Chapter 2 of *Life Science* describes how the body breaks down the food you eat into the organic molecules your cells need. Digestion begins in the mouth when you chew your food, and it mixes with saliva from the salivary glands. Saliva contains enzymes such as amylase, a protein that speeds up the chemical process of digestion. The enzymes break down complex carbohydrates, such as the starch in crackers, into simpler carbohydrates (sugars). Recall (Activity 9) that iodine is a *reagent* (a substance used to detect the present of another substance) for detecting starch.

Notice all the scientific claims in the previous paragraph—the enzymes in saliva, starches being broken down into sugars, and so on. This activity is all about verifying those claims for yourself.

Objectives

- Observe an enzyme-facilitated reaction.
- Experimentally verify several scientific claims.

Skills

- Drawing conclusions from observations and experimental results

Materials (per group of 2–4)

- unsalted saltine crackers (2)
- plastic bag, small
- iodine in dropper bottle
- paper plate, white
- bowl or beaker, small, transparent, colorless
- paper towel or white work surface
- water

Procedure

1. Place the beaker or bowl of water on a white surface. Add a few drops of iodine to the water. Record the color in the table below. In the fourth column, write what the color indicates.

2. Place one unsalted saltine cracker in a small plastic bag and crush it to fine crumbs.

3. Pile the crumbs on one side of a white paper plate and test them with a drop or two of iodine.

4. Record the color of the iodine in the table below. Write what the color indicates.

5. Choose a team member who can chew a cracker for a long time without being grossed out. Try to work up a good amount of saliva in your mouth. Then bite off about a quarter of the second cracker and

chew it up completely until it completely liquifies. Don't swallow. Keep mixing the liquid in the mouth for an additional 2–3 minutes, until the liquid tastes sweet.

6. Spit a small pool of the liquified cracker onto the other side of the paper plate. Test the mess with a few drops of iodine.

7. Record the color of the iodine in the table below. Write what the color indicates.

Substance Tested	Color of Reagent	What is indicated? (presence or absence of starch)
water		
dry crushed cracker		
chewed up cracker		

8. Compare your results with those of your classmates. Do you think everyone produces the same amount of amylase enzymes in their saliva? Explain.

_____

_____

— Commonplace Space —

Iodine was discovered by French and English chemists in the early 19th century. However, its medical use for sterilizing wounds was introduced a century later in 1908 by Istrian-Italian surgeon Antonio Grossich. The name iodine comes from the Greek word iodes, meaning violet-colored. The image shows some iodine crystals creating a purple vapor inside a glass sphere.

Activity 14   Fermentation

Observing the Action of Yeast

Today's Date _____

General Information

Life Science text reference: Chapter 5, Section 5.3

45 minutes initial setup, 3 hours waiting while running experiment, 5 minutes collecting data at the end

Introduction

During cellular respiration, glucose reacts with oxygen to producing carbon dioxide, water, and ATP molecules. However, if oxygen is not available for respiration, some organisms and some types of cells can continue to convert food into energy by using the process of fermentation. Cells that use fermentation include many types of bacteria and archaea, yeasts, and muscle cells. When yeasts break down molecules of glucose, they produce carbon dioxide and ethyl alcohol as by-products. Given an adequate food supply, yeast cells reproduce by budding every 90 minutes or so, as shown in the accompanying image. A small bud forms and splits off to form a new daughter cell. In this activity, you observe, collect, and measure the gas produced by the fermentation of yeast.

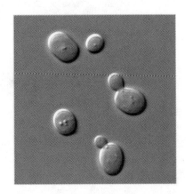

Objectives

- Observe the process and products of fermentation.

Skills

- Measuring and recording data
- Identifying signs of population growth

Materials (for the class)

- plastic bottle, 1-liter, with cap (8 bottles; only 1 cap is required if the bottles are identical)
- plastic basin, approx. 15" × 13" × 8" deep
- rubber stopper, #3, 1-hole (4)
- silicone tubing, 5 mm OD, 20" (4)
- digital mass scale, 0.1 g resolution
- measuring cup, ½-liter
- measuring cup, 8 oz
- scoop or teaspoon measure
- small cup or bowl (4)
- small funnel
- active, dry baking yeast, ¼-oz packet (4)
- table sugar
- permanent marker
- tap water, 105°F
- baking thermometer (fast)
- bottle support materials: a short piece of wood and two paint stir sticks (see photo and teacher instructions)
- shipping tape
- plastic card

Procedure

1. Fill the basin with tap water to a depth of about 3 inches, so that when one of the 1-L bottles is placed horizontally in the water its mouth is completely submerged. Clamp a piece of wood across the basin to act as a support for the four gas collecting bottles. The image at the right illustrates this, along with the next few steps.

2. Prepare four 20-inch lengths of plastic tubing by firmly inserting one end of each length of tubing into a #3 stopper.

3. Fill a 1-L bottle with water to above the brim. Cover the top with a plastic card (such as a driver's license or credit card). Lay the bottle in the water in the basin and remove the card.

4. Thread the loose end of one of the lengths of tubing into the bottle about four inches.

5. Invert the bottle and hang the stopper over the side of the basin out of the way. You should see no air bubbles in the bottle.

6. Tape the bottle to the support material so that it remains upright.

7. Repeat steps 3–6 with three more 1-L bottles. Label the bottles #1, #2, #3, and #4.

8. Release the clamps on the support board and slide it with all the bottles to the end of the basin. Cut the paint stir sticks so they will lay flat on the bottom of the basin underneath the bottles. Tape the sticks together and put them in the water. Carefully lift the bottles just enough to slide the sticks under the bottles. This prevents the weight of the bottles from constricting the tubes.

9. Empty one packet of yeast into each of four small bowls or cups. Label the cups #1, #2, #3, and #4.

10. Using a digital mass balance that reads to at least one decimal, and a small scoop or teaspoon measure, measure out the following amounts of table sugar and add the sugar to each cup of yeast:
    a. #1: 0 g (none)
    b. #2: 1.0 g
    c. #3: 2.0 g
    d. #4: 3.0 g

11. Prepare four fermentation bottles: Use the marker to label the bottles 1–4. Pour 230 mL (8 oz) of warm water into each. The water temperature should be between 100°F and 110°F. If you have a sink with hot and cold taps, run the water until it is fully hot, then hold a fast digital baking thermometer in the running water and adjust the water temperature until the water is running at 105°F. Then measure out the amount of water for each bottle and put the water in the bottle.

12. Using a small funnel, pour the contents of cup #1 into fermentation bottle #1. Screw on the cap and shake the bottle a few seconds to mix the yeast thoroughly into the warm water. Remove the bottle cap and place the bottle in front of gas collecting bottle #1. Firmly stopper the yeast/fermentation bottle with the stopper connected to the tube inserted into collecting bottle #1. Repeat this procedure with bottle sets 2, 3, and 4.

13. Formulate and write below a hypothesis about the relative amounts of carbon dioxide you expect to collect in bottles 1–4.

Our Hypothesis

_____

_____

_____

14. Wait for the yeast to consume the sugar and produce carbon dioxide. You should see gas bubbling into the bottles within a few minutes. Check the setup occasionally to make sure everything is secure. The gas collection process with run for about three hours, when the yeast run out of food.

15. After the volume of gas in the bottles has stopped increasing, use a permanent marker to mark the water level on the side of each bottle. Be careful to mark on the bottles themselves and not on the tape securing the bottles to the support board.

16. Remove the gas collecting bottles and refill each one with water to the water-level mark. Then pour the water into a 500-mL measuring cup and measure the volume. The amounts of water are equal to the volumes of gas collected in each collecting bottle. Record the four gas volumes in a table in the data area below.

— Our Data —

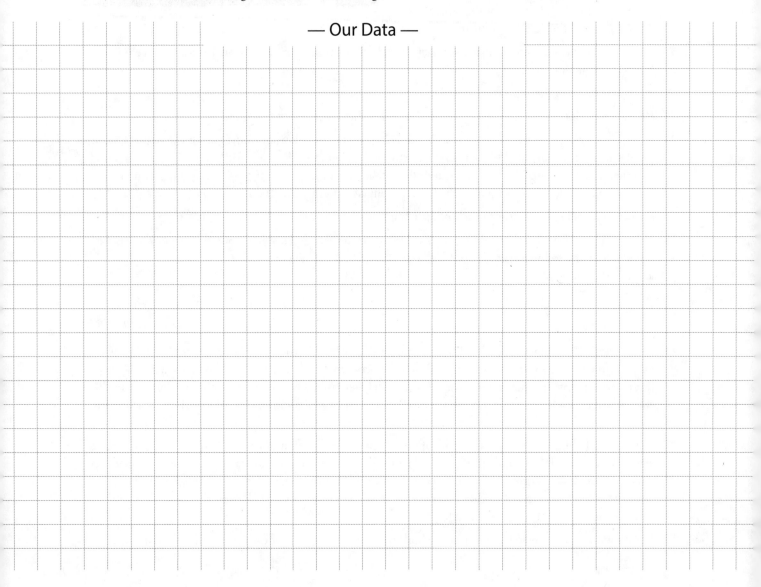

17. Beside the data table, make a bar chart showing the amount of gas collected in milliliters for each of bottles 1–4. On the chart, show two bars for each bottle: one bar for the amount of sugar, and another bar beside it showing the amount of gas collected. Write a description of your data below, describing the data and the shape of the chart.

_____

_____

_____

_____

18. What are the causes of the variation in the amounts of gas collected? (There is more than one.)

_____

_____

19. Do the data support your hypothesis? Explain below.

_____

_____

_____

_____

Yeast Feast

The sugar spreads out from the west to the east!
Each one of us joins in the wonderful feast!
Our passion for making this gas has increased
Or so it would seem to the yeast,
at least.

—John D. Mays

Activity 15 — Experimental Design

Testing for Variations in the Human Olfactory Sense

Today's Date _____

General Information

Life Science text reference: Chapter 6, Section 6.2

Estimated Time: 50 minutes

Introduction

The sense of smell may alert you to the pleasure of freshly baked bread or to the danger of a gas leak. It begins when molecules escape from a substance and float into your nose. The molecules dissolve in the watery mucous that covers a sheet of *olfactory epithelium* that lines the upper part of your nasal cavity. The dissolved molecules then bind to membrane receptors on the cilia of your olfactory receptor cells. The membrane receptors send impulses to neurons in the olfactory bulb and from there signals are passed along the olfactory tract to several areas in your brain. Because those areas have connections to the limbic system (important for emotional states and memory formation), a smell can activate intense feelings and memories. Signals that reach your frontal cortex allow you to recognize the odor and identify it.

The ability to detect odors varies widely among individuals. Small genetic differences can cause a person to be unable to detect a particular class of odors while other genetic differences can cause a person to have an unusually strong sense of smell. Colds or certain medicines can dampen the ability to smell. Previous experiences can affect an individual's reaction to certain odors. For example, a child who once got sick after eating hot dogs may feel nauseated whenever he smells hot dogs. Individuals also differ in the time it takes to develop *olfactory fatigue*, that is, when a person no longer perceives the odor, even though the source of the odor persists in the environment.

In this activity, you design an experiment for investigating one aspect of the sense of smell. Some comments are in order here on single- and double-blind experiments. If a subject (a person) knows how they are being treated in a research study, that knowledge can influence the outcome. In this activity, if a person knows what he is supposed to be smelling, it may bias his thinking about when and how he thinks he smells it. In a single-blind experiment, the research subjects do not know how they are being treated, and thus their knowledge of what is going on cannot bias the results.

Scientists have known for a long time that the researcher's own knowledge about who is being treated and how can also bias the results. To deal with this, double-blind research techniques were developed. In a double-blind experiment, neither the researchers nor the research subjects know who is being treated with what. Instead, an intermediate team of technicians are the only ones that know. This intermediate team identifies the subjects with a code and administers the treatments. When the researchers talk to the research subjects or perform tests, the researchers do not know whether the person they are talking to has received the experimental treatment or a conventional treatment (or a fake treatment that does nothing), and the research subject doesn't know either. Thus, no one's knowledge can bias the results. After the data have been collected and interpreted—the condition of subject A1 improved, the condition of person A2 remained unchanged, etc.—the intermediary technicians reveal who received which treatment.

Designing and implementing double-blind experiments takes a lot of time. It also requires four different groups of people—the researchers, the intermediary technicians, the research subjects receiving the new therapy being tested, and research subjects receiving a conventional therapy (or a fake therapy that does nothing). If you have the resources to design such an experiment, then do so! However, if your time and resources are limited, as is likely, you should design your experiment to include at least single-blind techniques—the people you are testing should not know in advance what they are being tested on. Design your experiment so that you ask questions without tipping off the answers. For example, don't ask a person to say when she is first able to smell the ammonia vapor. Instead, ask her to indicate when she is first able to smell anything at all. As another example, don't ask a person if he can identify the smell of peanut butter. Instead, ask him if he smells anything, and, if so, to identify what it is.

Objectives

- Practice implementing the Scientific Method.
- Form a testable hypothesis.
- Design an experiment.
- Draw conclusions based on experimental data.
- Implement single-blind research techniques.

Skills

- Making predictions
- Identifying factors that affect an experiment
- Collecting and interpreting data

Materials (per group of 2–4)

- opaque containers for odorants (at least 2, numbered and coded)
- several odorants for lab groups to select from
- timer

Procedure

Experiment Selection

Choose for your experiment one of the following variations in the ability to smell:

- determine whether subjects can identify odors in unmarked containers
- determine whether a person's sex influences how people detect odors
- test individual's abilities to identify odors in two-odor mixtures
- test olfactory fatigue time in minutes for at least two odor materials
- Indicate your choice.

Our Research Topic

_____

_____

Form a Hypothesis

Form a hypothesis that makes an appropriate, testable, detailed prediction for the experiment you choose. Write your hypothesis as an if-then statement, like this example:

If the dog comes in the house with wet feet, then the grass got watered.

Note that a good hypothesis is a prediction, it is testable, and it is quantitative and specific, so far as possible. In other words, the hypothesis should contain some details of the specific experimental criteria that will be used to judge whether the hypothesis is supported by the results. The example above could be made more quantitative and specific this way:

If the dog comes in the house with feet wet enough to leave visible footprints on the tile floor, then the grass was watered for at least 10 minutes within the past hour.

Our Hypothesis

_____

_____

_____

Develop Your Test Method

Determine how you will test your hypothesis by designing an experiment using the materials provided. Some things to consider include how you will manipulate the variable you are testing, how you will keep all other conditions constant, what each member of your team will be doing, what kind of data you will collect (what variables, what measurements), and how the data will be collected (equipment, instruments, procedures).

Smelling odors in a lab must be done in a specific, safe manner. Do not hold a container directly under your nose and sniff deeply. Instead, open the container and hold it about 15 inches away from your face. Use your other hand to fan or waft the scent gently from the container toward your nose. Breath normally and sniff gently.

Write your experimental procedure in the space below. List the measurements you will make, the conditions that you will control, and the data you will collect. Write your experimental design clearly so that another team could read it and repeat the experiment as you plan to do it.

Our Experimental Procedure

_____

_____

_____

_____

_____

_____

_____

_____

_____

_____

_____

_____

Run Your Experiment and Collect Data

— Our Data —

Discussion and Conclusion

After you have completed your experiment, use this section to describe your data and to consider how it relates to your hypothesis. Include these ideas:

a. What variable did you manipulate?
b. What did you find? How do the data show this?
c. Were you surprised by what you found?
d. How could you improve your experiment?

Explain whether your hypothesis was supported by the data, spell out what you learned, and judge whether your results were definitive or inconclusive. If they were inconclusive, try to specify ways the experiment could be improved to obtain more definitive results.

_____

_____

_____

_____

_____

_____

_____

_____

_____

_____

_____

_____

_____

_____

_____

_____

_____

_____

— Commonplace Space —

Then Jip went up to the front of the ship and smelt the wind; and he started muttering to himself, 'Tar; Spanish onions; kerosene oil; wet raincoats; crushed laurel-leaves; rubber burning; lace-curtains being washed—No, my mistake, lace-curtains hanging out to dry; and foxes—hundreds of 'em—cubs; and—'

'Can you really smell all those different things in this one wind?' asked the Doctor.

'Why, of course!' said Jip.

—Hugh Lofting, from *The Story of Doctor Dolittle*

Humans have approximately 400 different olfactory receptors. These work in different combinations to enable us to discern different odors. How many different odors? That is an interesting question. Research from the 1920s indicated that humans can discern about 10,000 different smells. This is a far lower degree of diversity that our other senses can handle. For example, humans can detect well over one million different colors. But a research study reported in the journal *Science* in 2014 indicates that humans may be able to distinguish over one trillion different odors, and maybe far more! But most of us don't use our sense of smell very much to navigate everyday life, and we are not aware that we possess such amazing capabilities.

Activity 16

Gravitropism

Plants and Gravity

Today's Date _____

General Information

Life Science text reference: Chapter 6, Section 6.3

Estimated Time: 10 minutes initial setup, 5 minutes for observation each day for several days, and 10 minutes on the last day

Introduction

In this activity, you observe geotropism, also called gravitropism—growth in response to the force of gravity.

Objectives

🌿 Observe the reaction of a plant sensory system to the force of gravity.

Skills

🌿 Observation and sketching

Materials (per group of 2–4)

🌿 small glass jars with lids (2) 🌿 clear tape
🌿 paper towel 🌿 pencil
🌿 radish seeds 🌿 water

Procedure

Note that lighting conditions are not important during either phase of this activity.

Germination of Seeds

1. Fold a paper towel in half four times to make 16 layers. Press the top of your small glass jar firmly into the paper towel layers to leave a circular indentation. Cut around the circle. Push the 16 layers of paper towel into the bottom of your small glass jar.

2. Soak the layers with water. Drain any excess water from the jar. Sprinkle four radish seeds on top of the paper towels. Seal the jar with the lid. Set the jar in a safe place until the seeds germinate. Seedlings are ready for the next phase when root hairs are visible.

Geotropism

3. Put a small amount of water in a second small glass jar and lay the jar on its side so that the water pools along the side of the jar but doesn't spill out.

4. Pick out a seedling with root hairs from the germination jar. Insert the seedling into the jar top first and lay it in the water.

5. Slowly tip the jar upright. You want the seedling to stick to the side of the jar so that it is upside down and out of the water. Close the lid tightly to prevent the water from evaporating.

6. Fasten a piece of clear tape to the outside of the jar. Trace the outline of the seedling onto the tape as a reference. Also, make a nice sketch of the seedling in the sketch area labeled Before.

7. Set your jar in a safe place and wait for 24 hours.

8. Make another nice sketch of your seedling to show how it looked after 24 hours.

Before ——————— Sketches ——————— After

9. Describe how your seedling grew in response to gravity.

_____

_____

_____

_____

The Tuft of Flowers

I went to turn the grass once after one
Who mowed it in the dew before the sun.

The dew was gone that made his blade so keen
Before I came to view the levelled scene.

I looked for him behind an isle of trees;
I listened for his whetstone on the breeze.

But he had gone his way, the grass all mown,
And I must be, as he had been,—alone,

"As all must be," I said within my heart,
"Whether they work together or apart."

But as I said it, swift there passed me by
On noiseless wing a bewildered butterfly,

Seeking with memories grown dim o'er night
Some resting flower of yesterday's delight.

And once I marked his flight go round and round,
As where some flower lay withering on the ground.

And then he flew as far as eye could see,
And then on tremulous wing came back to me.

I thought of questions that have no reply,
And would have turned to toss the grass to dry;

But he turned first, and led my eye to look
At a tall tuft of flowers beside a brook,

A leaping tongue of bloom the scythe had spared
Beside a reedy brook the scythe had bared.

I left my place to know them by their name,
Finding them butterfly weed when I came.

The mower in the dew had loved them thus,
By leaving them to flourish, not for us,

Nor yet to draw one thought of ours to him.
But from sheer morning gladness at the brim.

The butterfly and I had lit upon,
Nevertheless, a message from the dawn,

That made me hear the wakening birds around,
And hear his long scythe whispering to the ground,

And feel a spirit kindred to my own;
So that henceforth I worked no more alone;

But glad with him, I worked as with his aid,
And weary, sought at noon with him the shade;

And dreaming, as it were, held brotherly speech
With one whose thought I had not hoped to reach.

"Men work together," I told him from the heart,
"Whether they work together or apart."

—Robert Frost

— Commonplace Space —

Activity 17

Exponential Growth

Today's Date _____

General Information

Life Science text reference: Chapter 7, Section 7.2

Estimated Time: 15 minutes

Introduction

Ancient stories about the invention of chess often report that the inventor of the game, when offered a reward by his ruler, requested that he be given wheat in the following manner: One grain would be placed on the first square of the chessboard, two grains on the second, four on the third, eight on the fourth, and so on. The number of grains on each subsequent square was to be doubled. The ruler believed the request to be meager and easy to fulfill. Although it takes some time, the problem can be solved using simple addition: $1 + 2 + 4 + 8 + \ldots$ for the 64 squares.

Here is another way to consider this problem. Suppose you invented something really amazing and were offered your choice of two prizes: one million dollars immediately or one penny today, two pennies tomorrow, 4 pennies the next day, and so on for one month. The number of pennies you received each day would be double the number you received the day before. If you chose the pennies, how long would it take before you reached one dollar? One million dollars?

Bacteria, yeast, and cells grow by doubling everything they are made of and then dividing in half. Two new cells replace the original cell. Populations of larger organisms in healthy environments can also grow exponentially.

Objectives

▦ Describe the implications of exponential growth.

Skills

▦ Comparing models

Materials (per group of 2–4)

▦ tissue paper

Procedure

1. Take a thin sheet of paper to represent one cell.

2. Fold the sheet of paper in half. Each section represents one daughter cell. Record the number of cells in the table.

3. Fold the paper in half again. Record the number of daughter cells.

4. Repeat step 3 as many times as you can.

5. How many times could you fold the paper? _____

6. How did the number of cells change with each fold? _____

7. How thick did the paper get? _____

Fold #	Number of Cells
0	1
1	
2	
3	
4	
5	
6	
7	
8	

Making Comparisons

Suppose you began with a piece of paper that was 0.001 cm thick. If you could fold it 30 times, how thick do you think it would be? Just as each fold doubles the number of "cells," it also doubles the thickness of the paper. After 10 folds, the paper would be 1.024 cm thick. After 17 folds, the paper would be 131 cm thick (just over 4 feet!). Twenty-five folds would make the paper 33,554 cm or just over 1,100 feet thick—nearly as tall as the Empire State Building! After 30 folds, the paper would be 6.67 miles high, about the height that planes fly! Use the space below to make a graph of 10 folds of paper.

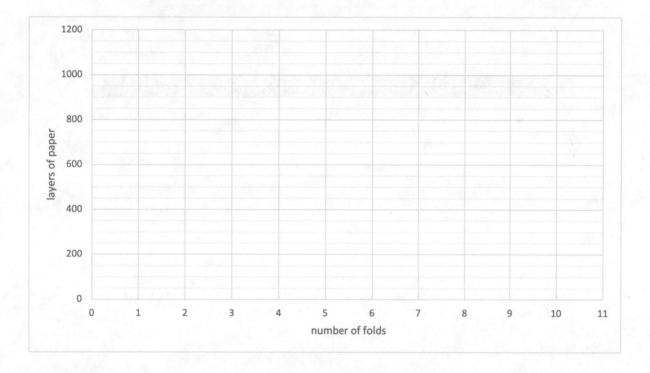

Proposed Explanations

Each of these models (the doubling pennies and the folding of paper) is useful for thinking about the complex process of exponential growth. Some parts of each model work better to demonstrate the process than other parts of each model. Compare the paper-folding model with the penny-doubling model. In each model, how does the number of items (pennies, paper sections, or layers) change?

_____

_____

How is the penny model like cell division? How is it different?

_____

_____

_____

_____

How is the paper-folding model like cell division? How is it different?

_____

_____

_____

_____

— Commonplace Space —

One of the most stunning instances of mathematics appearing in nature is the famous Fibonacci sequence:

1, 1, 2, 3, 5, 8, 13, 21, 34, 55, …

After the first two ones, each subsequent value in the sequence is determined by adding the two previous entries:

1 + 1 = 2; 2 + 1 = 3; 3 + 2 = 5; and so on.

The Fibonacci sequence appears in hundreds of ways in nature, a fact that has fascinated people for centuries. The numbers of spirals on pinecones, pineapples, and flower seedheads (and many other things) are always Fibonacci numbers. Moreover, as the yellow chamomile picture shows, the spirals often go in two (or more) different directions, and the numbers of spirals in the two different directions are always adjacent Fibonacci numbers (such as 34 and 55).

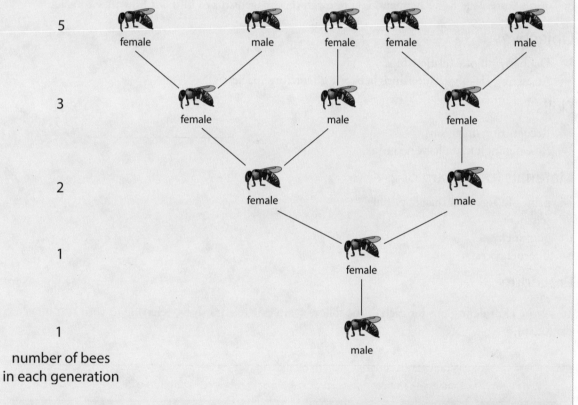

number of bees
in each generation

The generations of the honeybee are another instance where the Fibonacci sequence turns up. Male drones have one parent (a female), while female workers have two parents (a male and a female). This means that the numbers of parents, grandparents, etc. in the genetic lineage of a honeybee are the numbers in the Fibonacci sequence, as the diagram shows.

The spiral created by curving through adjacent boxes with sides equal to the numbers in the Fibonacci sequence closely models the shape of the nautilus. And these examples merely scratch the surface! Get your own pineapple or pinecone and see for yourself!

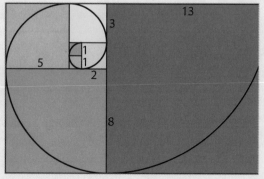

Activity 18

Classifying Interdependent Relationships

Today's Date _____

General Information

Life Science text reference: Chapter 7, Section 7.3

Estimated Time: 15 minutes

Introduction

In this activity, you practice identifying different types of symbiotic relationships between organisms. Some organisms you may not recognize. You also may not immediately recognize the symbiotic relationships that occur in nature. When this happens, you research these organisms to find out how they interact.

Objectives

- Define symbiotic relationships.
- Assess and classify relationships between interacting species.

Skills

- Recognizing organisms
- Researching unfamiliar organisms

Materials (per group of 2–4)

- print of Organism Images pdf file
- scissors
- glue stick
- internet access

Procedure

1. Write clear definitions for each of the follow symbiotic relationships, referring to your text if necessary:
parasitism:

_____

_____

_____

commensalism:

_____

_____

_____

mutualism:

_____

_____

_____

2. Cut apart the pictures of organisms provided. Match these organisms in pairs, based on how they are known to interact with one another in nature. Glue the pairs in the appropriate columns below. If you are unfamiliar with any of these organisms, set them aside.

3. Research any organisms that you have set aside. When you have identified relationships between them, glue them to in the appropriate column.

Parasitism	Commensalism	Mutualism

One of the most notorious parasites in history is *Plasmodium falciparum*, the cause of most human malaria. Evidence of the disease goes way back: 30 million years (from mosquitoes preserved in amber); ancient Egypt (from DNA tests); and according to a 2002 article in *Nature*, the earliest confirmed case occurred in AD 450 in Rome, based on DNA evidence from a children's cemetery. Malaria continues to infect over 200 million people per year, resulting in around 600,000 deaths annually. It is often claimed that over half of all the human deaths in history were due to malaria. This claim is apparently exaggerated. Nevertheless, malaria has claimed an enormous number of human lives and scientific research on malaria is a big deal.

In the early 20th century, researchers determined that the parasite that causes malaria is transmitted in humans by mosquito bites. By the 1950s, the scientific community thought the battle with malaria was over because spraying with DDT had been found to be very effective in controlling the mosquitos. Then it was discovered that DDT is devastating to the overall environment, with effects not just limited to mosquitoes, and its use was mostly discontinued. Since then, there have been many hopeful weapons against malaria, but no magic bullets. In fact, the parasite continues to develop resistance to the most widely used drugs. In the 1980s, work on a children's vaccine began. A moderately successful vaccine called RTS,S has now been developed and was approved in 2021 by the World Health Organization. So far, the efficacy of the RTS,S vaccine is in the range of 26–50%. But malaria is such a major global killer that continued work on more effective vaccines will continue.

— Commonplace Space —

Activity 19

Modeling Food Webs

Today's Date _____

General Information

Life Science text reference: Chapter 8, Sections 8.1 and 8.2

Estimated Time: 30–40 minutes

Introduction

Organisms use energy for life processes including movement, growth, tissue repair, cell division, and protein synthesis. The primary source of energy in most ecosystems is the sun, which producers use to make food. Consumers gain both matter and energy by consuming other organisms. The network of relationships that forms in an ecosystem is complex, and some organisms play special roles in preserving the balance. In this activity, you use role play to create a model of energy transfer in a food web and then explore the effects on the model of the loss of various feeding relationships.

Objectives

- Visualize food webs.
- Describe the potential impact that the loss of a species can have on an ecosystem.

Skills

- Identifying feeding relationships

Materials (per group of 2–4)

- organism name tags, prewritten
- yarn, 5-ft lengths (green, yellow, red, white, light blue, and dark blue)
- scissors

Procedure

This activity is designed to be performed in person, with at least a dozen students in a class. Modify the procedure if fewer students are involved or if the group is meeting in a virtual classroom.

1. Each student receives a name tag from the instructor. One student will be the sun; other students will be various organisms (grasses, grasshoppers, mice, rabbits, rats, robins, hawks, coyotes, millipedes, worms, decaying pumpkins, and fungi).

2. Consider your name tag and decide whether you are a producer or a consumer. If you are a consumer, decide whether you are primary (herbivore), secondary (carnivore), tertiary (apex predator), both primary and secondary (omnivore), or a decomposer. Obtain a five-foot string of yarn in the appropriate color:
   - sun—yellow
   - producer—green
   - primary consumer—light blue
   - secondary consumer—red
   - tertiary consumer—white
   - decomposer—dark blue
   - omnivore (primary and secondary consumer)—take two pieces of yarn, one light blue and one red

3. Move to a fairly open space, holding your yarn in one hand.

4. With the other hand, do the following:
    • Producers take the other end of the sun's yarn.
    • Primary consumers take the other end of the yarn held by the producer they would most likely eat.
    • Secondary consumers take the other end of the yarn held by the primary consumer they would most likely eat.
    • Tertiary consumers take the other end of the yarn held by the secondary consumer they would most likely eat.

5. Each student should now take note of your own name and the name(s) of the other(s) you are connected to and remember them for later documentation. Take some time to discuss the completed web. Focus on resolving any uncertainties in the relationships established.

6. Select one student to make a prediction about what will happen when one organism is removed.

7. Remove the organism nominated in step 6. Try to re-establish the food web. Discuss which of the remaining organisms were affected by the loss of one.

8. Repeat steps 6 and 7 with producers, primary consumers, secondary consumers, tertiary consumers, and decomposers.

9. Discuss how the loss of a primary consumer affects other organisms.

10. Discuss how the loss of decomposers affects other organisms.

Exercises

1. Who were you and who were you connected to?

    _____

    _____

2. Describe the effects on the ecosystem when a primary consumer was lost.

    _____

    _____

    _____

3. Describe the effects on the ecosystem when a decomposer was lost.

    _____

    _____

Although named millipede from the Latin for "thousand feet," no millipede was known to have more than a few hundred legs until the discovery of this creature in 2021 in Australia. (Of course, it was Australia, the land with the strangest and scariest of creatures.) This female millipede has 1,306 legs, making it the first millipede to live up to its name. They live in deep drill holes, between 15 m (50 ft) and 60 m (200 ft) below the surface. The species was imaginatively named *Eumillipes persephone*. The first part of the name (the genus) means "true millipede." The second part (species) comes from ancient Greek mythology. Persephone was the daughter of Zeus and Demeter. She became the Queen of the underworld after being abducted by Hades, the king of the underworld.

Activity 20

Conducting Research

Today's Date _____

General Information

Life Science text reference: Chapter 8, Section 8.3

Estimated Time: 2 hours outside of class; 1 class period for presentations

Introduction

Organisms use energy for life processes such as movement, growth, tissue repair, cell division, and protein synthesis. The primary source of energy in most ecosystems is the sun. Organisms gain both matter and energy by consuming other organisms. Some energy is lost as heat at each trophic level. In this activity, you research an ecosystem and create a PowerPoint or Google Slides presentation to share with your class.

Objectives

- Compare food webs in different ecosystems.
- Explain how environmental conditions and human activities affect food webs.

Skills

- Conducting research
- Making presentations

Materials (per student or student group of up to 6 students)

- laptop computer with presentation software and internet access

Procedure

1. Students will either choose or be assigned one of the following ecosystems to research: salt marsh, tropical rainforest, grassland, still water, river and stream, taiga.

2. Identify a food web within your assigned ecosystem. Prepare a slide show to share with the class at the close of this activity. The presentation must contain a minimum of five slides and should require 10–12 minutes to present. If you are working in groups, each student must present at least one slide. Keep in mind these guidelines for your slides:
   a. Use brief bullet points to summarize information. You should have more to say than the bullet on the screen says.
   b. Include one or two images on each slide.
   c. Use a large font that is easy to read on a screen.
   d. Adding fancy colors and animations is fun, but not required for full credit. You may keep it simple if you choose.

3. As you gather information about your topic, keep track of the sources of that information. You will need to include a Works Cited slide in your presentation. For guidance on citations, refer to a style guide or website such as https://owl.english.purdue.edu/owl/resource/747/24/.

4. Points to research:
   a. the trophic level of each participant in the web

b. the flow of energy among organisms in the ecosystem
c. the proportion of energy transferred from one trophic level to the next
d. the potential impact, either positive or negative, of specific human activities on the food web

5. Refer to the Grading Rubric below for guidance as you plan your slides.
6. Write an outline of each proposed slide. Turn it in on the date required by your instructor.
7. Use the feedback your teacher provides on your outline to complete any further research, to modify your slides, or to make additions to your presentation.
8. Present your slide show.

Grading Rubric for Ecosystem Food-Web Presentation			
	10 points	6 points	2 points
Trophic Level of Each Organism	Trophic level of each participant in the web is defined.	Trophic level of one or two participants is missing or incorrect.	Trophic level of more than two participants is missing or incorrect.
Flow of Energy	The flow of energy through the food web is well described.	The flow of energy is described with one or two omissions or errors.	The flow of energy is not well described.
Energy Lost at Each Level	The amount of energy that reaches each successive trophic level is thoroughly explained.	The amount of energy that reaches each successive trophic level is briefly explained.	The amount of energy that reaches each successive trophic level is explained with errors.
Impact of Human Activity	The potential impact, either positive or negative, of human activities on the food web is thoroughly explained.	The potential impact, either positive or negative, of human activities on the food web is briefly explained.	The potential impact, either positive or negative, of human activities on the food web is not explained.
Organization	All slides are as outlined, and the organization of information is clear.	All slides are as outlined, but the order is confusing.	The slides are not in order and information is missing that should have been included.
Text	There is just enough text on the slides to make the point.	There is one slide with either too much or not enough text on it.	There are 2 or more slides that have too much or not enough text on them.
Oral Presentation	Presenter had an organized verbal presentation that added information to the bullets on the slides.	Presenter read, almost verbatim, the text on the slides without adding anything.	Presenter spoke off topic from the slides and added nothing to the bulleted information.
Presence	Voice was loud enough to hear, speaker seemed prepared, and proper formal speech was used.	Speaker was prepared but either vocal volume or speech was not appropriate.	Speaker was not prepared, and vocal volume or speech was not appropriate.
Slide Layout	Slides were clear and contained images related to the topic.	Slides were clear but did not contain images related to the topic.	Slides were messy with overlapping elements and/or no images.
Grammar, Spelling, and Mechanics	Slides contained no errors.	Slides contained one or two errors.	Slides contained three or more errors.

— Commonplace Space —

The Wild Swans at Coole

The trees are in their autumn beauty,
The woodland paths are dry,
Under the October twilight the water
Mirrors a still sky;
Upon the brimming water among the stones
Are nine-and-fifty swans.

The nineteenth autumn has come upon me
Since I first made my count;
I saw, before I had well finished,
All suddenly mount
And scatter wheeling in great broken rings
Upon their clamorous wings.

I have looked upon those brilliant creatures,
And now my heart is sore.
All's changed since I, hearing at twilight,
The first time on this shore,

The bell-beat of their wings above my head,
Trod with a lighter tread.

Unwearied still, lover by lover,
They paddle in the cold
Companionable streams or climb the air;
Their hearts have not grown old;
Passion or conquest, wander where they will,
Attend upon them still.

But now they drift on the still water,
Mysterious, beautiful;
Among what rushes will they build,
By what lake's edge or pool
Delight men's eyes when I awake some day
To find they have flown away?

—William Butler Yeats

Activity 21

What's it Like Where You Live?

Today's Date _____

General Information

Life Science text reference: Chapter 9, Sections 9.2 and 9.3

Estimated Time: 40 minutes

Introduction

Every habitat contains specific geographical conditions shaped by climate and weather. Climate, in turn, is shaped by global patterns of solar energy, air flow, and geographical features such as mountains and large bodies of water. The goal in this activity is to investigate the climate and weather of the region where you live, and to discover the unique features that species in your area have adapted to.

Objectives

- Identify features of local geography that relate to weather patterns.
- Classify the climate in your region.
- Identify the unique features affecting habitat where you live.

Skills

- Identify weather patterns
- Conducting research
- Using library resources

Materials (for the class)

- computer and internet access
- library access (optional)

Procedure

Research your local climate and weather patterns. You can make use of the internet only, or also take a trip to the library to explore resources such as books, magazine articles, newspaper articles, pamphlets, and personal interviews. Use the space below to describe two or more features of local geography, to relate local geography to weather patterns, to describe local weather patterns, and to describe your local climate. Also name major biome types in your area.

My Research Results

Our location is:

_____

Our local geography includes these unique features:

_____

_____

_____

Our local weather patterns can be described as follows:

_____

_____

_____

_____

Our climate consists of these temperature and precipitation norms:

_____

_____

The features of our local geography affect the weather patterns and climate in these specific ways:

_____

_____

_____

_____

The major biome types in our area include these:

_____

_____

_____

_____

June 30. Half cloudy, half sunny, clouds lustrous white. The tall pines crowded along the top of the Pilot Peak Ridge look like six-inch miniatures exquisitely outlined on the satiny sky. Average cloudiness for the day about .25. No rain. And so this memorable month ends, a stream of beauty unmeasured, no more to be sectioned off by almanac arithmetic than sun-radiance or the currents of seas and rivers—a peaceful, joyful stream of beauty. Every morning, arising from the death of sleep, the happy plants and all our fellow animal creatures great and small, and even the rocks, seemed to be shouting, "Awake, awake, rejoice, rejoice, come love us and join in our song. Come! Come!" Looking back through the stillness and romantic enchanting beauty and peace of the camp grove, this June seems the greatest of all months of my life, the most truly, divinely free, boundless like eternity, immortal. Everything in it seems equally divine—one smooth, pure, wild glow of Heaven's love, never to be blotted or blurred by anything past or to come.

—John Muir, from *My First Summer in the Sierra*

Activity 22

Experimenting with Shrimp Hatcheries

Today's Date _____

General Information

Life Science text reference: Chapter 9, Section 9.3

Estimated Time: 30 minutes to setup; 5 minutes daily for observation and recording data

Introduction

Although they are crustaceans, brine shrimp are not really shrimp. They are members of a group of organisms called *branchiopods*. Brine shrimp live in highly salty water and look much like tiny shrimp. They are often found in small, evaporating saltwater puddles. As water evaporates, the puddle becomes increasingly salty. Brine shrimp have short life spans. In the time it takes for a puddle to evaporate, they can hatch, grow to adulthood, mate, and lay eggs. The eggs can lie dormant in the dried sediment until the water returns. In this activity, you design an experiment to determine the ideal biome for hatching brine shrimp eggs. To test the ideal saltiness for the hatching of brine shrimp, you perform a serial dilution in which you create solutions of salt water that vary in concentration.

Objectives

- Practice using the Scientific Method.
- Make conclusions based on data you collect.

Skills

- Performing serial dilutions
- Collecting and interpreting data

Materials (per student or student group of up to 6 students)

- brine shrimp eggs, 0.2 g
- table salt, non-iodized, 4.5 tsp
- measuring cup
- distilled water
- graduated cylinder, 100 mL
- small jars with lids (5)
- marking pen
- small spoon
- masking tape
- safety glasses

Procedure

1. Using masking tape and a marking pen, label the five small jars as follows: "0.2 g/mL," "0.02 g/mL," "0.002 g/mL," "0.0002 g/mL," and "distilled water."

2. Perform a serial dilution to create solutions of salt water that vary in concentration from 0.2 g/mL down to 0.0002 g/mL. Each solution will be less salty than the one before by a factor of 10. Put on your safety glasses. Measure out 4.5 tsp of sodium chloride (non-iodized table salt) into your measuring cup. Add distilled water to the cup until the volume reaches 100 mL. Stir the solution until the salt is fully dissolved.

3. Pour 10 mL of the solution of salty water from the measuring cup into the graduated cylinder. Pour the remaining 90 mL of solution into the small jar labeled "0.2 g/mL."

4. Pour the 10 mL of salty water from the graduated cylinder back into the measuring cup. Add distilled water to the cup until the volume reaches 100 mL. Stir the solution.

5. Pour 10 mL of the new solution of salty water from the measuring cup into the graduated cylinder. Pour the remaining 90 mL of solution into the small jar labeled "0.02 g/mL."

6. Pour the 10 mL of salty water from the graduated cylinder back into the measuring cup. Add distilled water to the cup until the volume reaches 100 mL. Stir the solution.

7. Pour 10 mL of the new solution of salty water from the measuring cup into the graduated cylinder. Pour the remaining 90 mL of solution into the small jar labeled "0.002 g/mL."

8. Pour the 10 mL of salty water from the graduated cylinder back into the measuring cup. Add distilled water to the cup until the volume reaches 100 mL. Stir the solution.

9. Pour 10 mL of the new solution of salty water from the measuring cup into the graduated cylinder. Pour the remaining 90 mL of solution into the small jar labeled "0.0002 g/mL."

10. Discard the remaining 10 mL of solution from the graduated cylinder. Rinse the graduated cylinder and the measuring cup with distilled water.

11. Measure 90 mL of distilled water into the measuring cup. Pour this into the jar labeled "distilled water."

12. Divide your brine shrimp eggs into five equal groups. Place one group of eggs into each jar. Cap the jars tightly.

13. Place your jars in a reasonably warm spot (20–30°C, or 68–86°F) away from direct sunlight and let them incubate for about 30 days.

14. Assuming today is day 0, determine the dates of the days listed in the following table. Check your experiment on those dates. Without disturbing the eggs at the bottom of the jars, hold them up to a light source, such as a window. Look for tiny, whitish larvae swimming with a jerky motion. These larvae are called nauplii (singular, nauplius).

15. Record your observations as follows: record growth as "+" and no growth as "–." Record the presence of more than 10 nauplii as "++." If more than one jar shows growth on a given day, record the jar containing the most brine shrimp as "+++." Only count swimming larvae.

16. When you have completed the experiment, clean up by pouring the brine shrimp down the sink.

Day	Date	0.2 g/mL	0.02 g/mL	0.002 g/mL	0.0002 g/mL	H$_2$O
1						
2						
4						
8						
12						
15						

Analysis

What is the lowest salt concentration that is suitable for hatching brine shrimp eggs?

_____

What is the highest salt concentration that is suitable for hatching brine shrimp eggs?

_____

At what concentration do the brine shrimp survive the longest?

_____

Which solution appears to be the most suitable niche for brine shrimp? Explain your answer.

_____

The salinity of ocean water salinity averages about 0.035 g/mL. How does this compare to the salinity brine shrimp are adapted to?

_____

_____

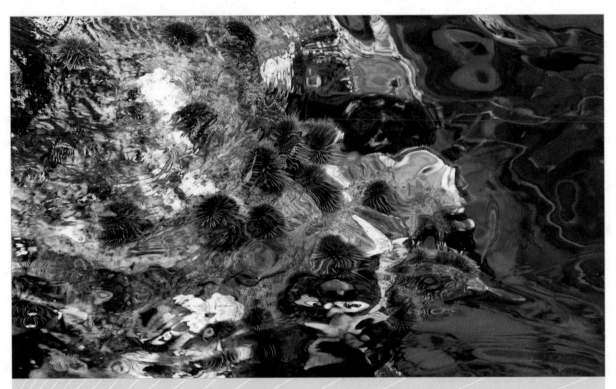

Each of them in his own tempo and with his own voice discovered and reaffirmed with astonishment the knowledge that all things are one thing and that one thing is all things—plankton, a shimmering phosphorescence on the sea and the spinning planets and an expanding universe, all bound together by the elastic string of time. It is advisable to look from the tide pool to the stars and then back to the tide pool again.

—John Steinbeck, from *The Log from the Sea of Cortez*

— Commonplace Space —

Activity 23

Design a Self-Sustaining Ecosystem

Aquarium and Terrarium

Today's Date _____

General Information

Life Science text reference: Chapter 10, Section 10.1

Estimated Time: 50 minutes

Introduction

An ecosystem is a community of different species that interact with each other and with the environment. The abiotic factors of an ecosystem include water, soil, weather, temperature, and humidity. The biotic factors include producers, consumers, and decomposers. The organisms fulfilling these roles must be in balance for the ecosystem to thrive. In this activity, you design a closed ecosystem, either aquatic or terrestrial, that will feed, clean, and restore itself.

Objectives

- Describe the elements necessary to a balanced ecosystem.
- Design an ecosystem.

Skills

- Thinking critically about ecosystems
- Conducting research
- Communicating results

Materials (per group of 2 students)

- computer and internet access

Procedure

1. **Research**. Choose whether you want to design an aquarium or a terrarium. Then do some research to learn what kinds of organisms can survive in and support a self-sustaining system. Consider the following:
   a. **Plants**. The right plants grow well, but not too well. They are hardy and pest/disease resistant. They provide enough plant biomass to sustain efficient life cycles and, in a terrarium, to support the water cycle.
   b. **Container.** Think about how big your container must be to allow for proper circulation of oxygen and carbon dioxide.
   c. **Light**. Discover what the best lighting conditions are for your ecosystem.
   d. **Water.** Learn what the best source of water is for your ecosystem. What things must you consider about water drainage if you choose to design a terrarium? How will you keep the water clean if you are setting up an aquarium?
   e. **Animals**. What kinds of aquatic animals can survive and thrive in a closed system?
   f. **Decomposers.** What can you put in your closed system to manage breaking down wastes?

_____

_____

The term ecosystem was first introduced in 1935 by English botanist Sir Arthur George Tansley in describing the exchange of materials between organisms and their environment. Tansley was the founding editor of the Journal of Ecology. He was inducted in the British Royal Society in 1915 and knighted in 1950.

Nature, in its ministry to man, is not only the material, but is also the process and the result. All the parts incessantly work into each other's hands for the profit of man. The wind sows the seed; the sun evaporates the sea; the wind blows the vapor to the field; the ice, on the other side of the planet, condenses rain on this; the rain feeds the plant; the plant feeds the animal; and thus the endless circulations of the divine charity nourish man.

—Ralph Waldo Emerson, from *Nature*

_____

_____

_____

_____

2. Energy in your Ecosystem. Based on the flow of energy and biomass in an ecosystem, determine the proportion of producers to consumers and/or decomposers you need. Write down what you require and explain your reasoning.

_____

_____

_____

_____

_____

3. Sketch your Ecosystem. In the space below, make a sketch of your proposed self-sustaining ecosystem and label each component.

Sketches

— Commonplace Space —

Activity 24

Modeling Earth Processes

Plate Tectonics, Weathering, Erosion, and Sedimentation

Today's Date _____

General Information

Life Science text reference: Chapter 11, Section 11.1

Estimated Time: 30 minutes

Introduction

Chapter 11 of *Life Science* describes the fossil record and some of the earliest scientists to study geological processes. In this activity, you investigate the geological processes that play a part in the formation and eventual discovery of fossils.

The processes of plate tectonics, weathering, erosion, and sedimentation rarely occur together in nature, but when they do the results can be very dramatic. In this experiment, you model the geologic conditions that have shaped many coastal regions when a continent sits on the edge of a tectonic plate, and that plate overrides another tectonic plate in a process known as *subduction*. After the continent is forced upward by the subduction, you then explore how weather and erosion tear down the sharply sculpted features of the uplifted mountain chain to a much more rounded landmass. Finally, you see how the rock and mineral particles that have been eroded from the landmass are sorted by the amount of energy that is available for transporting the grains of various size, shape, and mass.

Andes Mountains

Objectives

🌋 Model the building of mountain chains by tectonic forces.
🌋 Model weathering and erosion.
🌋 Observe how wind and water sort rock and mineral particles.

Skills

🌋 Comparing models with geographical formations
🌋 Writing descriptions

Materials (per group of 2–4)

🌋 sand, two cups
🌋 baking soda, two cups
🌋 gravel, two cups

🌋 gloves
🌋 large tray
🌋 garden trowel

🌋 water in spray bottle
🌋 vinegar

Procedure

1. Place two cups each of sand, baking soda, and gravel in a large tray. Blend the dry materials with gloved hands. Cover the bottom of the tray evenly with the mixed materials.

2. **Subduction event:** Use the trowel and gloved hands to shape the particles into a steep-walled cliff backed by a mountain chain with a sharp ridgeline. Lightly spray water on the particles as you work. The spraying with water models the ocean water acting as a lubricant for the subduction event. When you are finished, about half the tray (lengthwise) should be scraped clean of particles, and your mountain chain and cliff should be running along the other half (lengthwise).

Appalachian Mountains

3. Describe the appearance of your landform after the tectonic force is applied. Study the images of six different mountain chains and list four that exhibit features similar to your formations.

4. **Chemical weathering** and erosion: Use the wash bottle to pour vinegar in small increments along the length of the mountain ridgeline.

Mount Everest in the Himalaya Mountains

5. Describe the appearance of the mountain chain after the weathering and erosion events. Explain what caused chemical weathering and what caused erosion. List two mountain chains from the images that display similar features today.

_____

_____

_____

_____

_____

_____

6. Examine the erosion pattern on the "ocean" side of the mountain. It may be similar to the alluvial fan image shown here. Describe the size of particles and the distance they have traveled from the mountain. Which type of particle would require more water or wind energy for transportation?

_____

_____

_____

_____

7. What type of rock strata would be more likely to form caves: sandstone or limestone? Why?

_____

_____

8. Explain whether the changes you observed were reversible or irreversible and give reasons for your classification.

_____

_____

_____

_____

_____

_____

Ozark Mountais

Swiss Alps

Rocky Mountains

Sierra Nevada
could lift the heart so high
fault block uplift
thrust of westward slipping crust—one way
to raise and swing the clouds around—
thus pine trees leapfrog up on sunlight

trapped in cells of leaf—nutrient minerals called together
like magic song
to lead a cedar log along, that hopes
to get to sea at last and be
a great canoe.

—Gary Snyder, from "The Flowing"

DNA Construction and Replication

Today's Date _____

General Information

Life Science text reference: Chapter 12, Section 12.1

Estimated Time: 30 minutes

Introduction

The DNA molecule is made of individual nucleotides. Each nucleotide consists of a sugar (deoxyribose), a phosphate group, and a nitrogen-containing organic base. There are four basic types of DNA nucleotides—adenine, thymine, guanine, and cytosine—that are named according to the bases they contain. Each DNA molecule consists of two chains of millions of nucleotides arranged in a specific pattern that codes for the proteins needed to regulate a living cell. The nitrogen bases of each strand bond with their pairs on the other strand. The two strands twist together in a double-helix shape that resembles a spiral staircase. In this activity, you model DNA construction and the process of the DNA molecule making a copy of itself, a process called *replication*.

Objectives

- Describe the contents of a nucleotide.
- Describe the structure of the DNA molecule.
- Model the processes of DNA construction and replication.

Skills

- Recognizing the way base pairs match
- Using a model to increase understanding

Materials (per group of 2 students)

- printed sheet of DNA model pieces
- white paper (2 sheets)
- cardstock (1 sheet)
- scissors
- glue stick
- clear plastic report cover (1)
- cellophane tape

Procedure

1. **Nucleotide Construction.** Glue the page of DNA model pieces onto a piece of cardstock to make the pieces stiffer and easier to work with. Then cut apart the pieces.

2. Cut the report cover in half along the side to make two 8 ½ " × 11" pieces of plastic. Lay each sheet of plastic on top of each sheet of plain white paper to give you a glossy surface on which to work.

3. Using tape to represent the bonds between phosphate groups, sugar, and nitrogen bases, build DNA nucleotides in the arrangements shown. Orient the pieces so the labels are right-side-up and attach the sugar to the square end of the base. Place the tape underneath the pieces, sticky side up. You will have 16 left-hand models and 16 right-hand models.

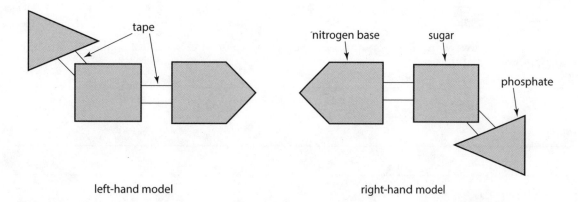

left-hand model   right-hand model

4. **DNA Construction.** Make a vertical chain of left-hand nucleotides using the following sequence: A, T, C, G, T, G, A, C from top to bottom. Match these nucleotides with their right-hand complements. When nucleotides bond, the phosphate of one nucleotide bonds with the sugar of its neighbor. Use short pieces of tape to make this bond. When chains of nucleotides bond to each other, a weak hydrogen bond joins the two complementary bases. Make this week bond with tape.

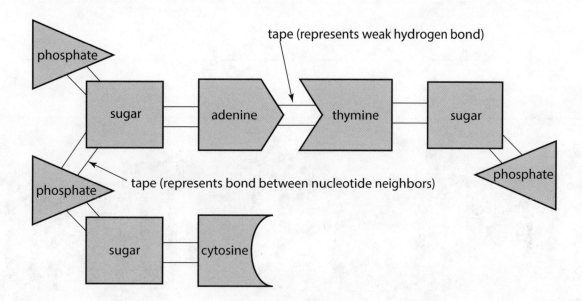

5. **DNA Replication.** You should now have a DNA model with 8 pairs of bases. Because adenine only pairs with thymine and cytosine only pairs with guanine, base pairing ensures that DNA is duplicated exactly during replication. Demonstrate the process of replication with your model. Using your scissors to represent the enzyme system that breaks the hydrogen bonds between the bases, separate the left and right chains of DNA.

6. In the nucleus of a replicating cell, free DNA nucleotides bond with the newly separated chains. Use your free nucleotides to build new complementary chains for the original left and right strands. When you are done, you should have two identical double-stranded DNA molecules. This replication process within a cell allows daughter cells to be exactly like the parent cell from which they came.

Exercises

1. On the lines below, write a paragraph that explains the purpose of DNA and describes the structure of the DNA molecule.

   _____

   _____

   _____

   _____

   _____

   _____

2. On the lines below, write a paragraph that explains how DNA is able to copy itself exactly.

   _____

   _____

   _____

   _____

   _____

   _____

The discovery of the structure of the DNA molecule in 1953 marked the beginning of the field of molecular biology. The story involves drama, intrigue, brilliance, and a sad ending. The drama is due to the fact that James Watson and Francis Crick, the two scientists usually credited with figuring out the molecule's structure, were not the only ones working on the problem at the time, and there was fierce competition to be first. Watson and Crick had some good ideas but lacked essential data from molecular X-rays of DNA, available using a technique called X-ray crystallography. Through a strange sequence of events, Watson and Crick were able to see a key X-ray image shown to them by Maurice Wilkins, a scientist working with Rosalind Franklin, who owned the photo, and who had done a lot of work on DNA herself. The intrigue comes in because there is evidence that the photo was shown to Watson and Crick without Franklin's knowledge or consent. The brilliance in the story is, of course, that Watson and Crick did figure out the enormously complex structure of the molecule. (They built a large wood and metal model of it—even the pros build models!) In 1962, Watson, Crick, and Wilkins were awarded the Nobel Prize in Physiology or Medicine for their discovery. (As it happens, John Steinbeck, quoted on p. 72, received the Nobel Prize for Literature the same year.) Finally, the sad ending lies in the fact that since the Nobel Prize is only awarded to living persons—Rosalind Franklin could not share in the prize; she had died of cancer at the age of 38, four years earlier.

— **Commonplace Space** —

Activity 26

Investigating a Genetic Bottleneck

Changes to Gene Pools

Today's Date _____

General Information

Life Science text reference: Chapter 12, Section 12.3

Estimated Time: 30 minutes

Introduction

Within any population of organisms, the frequency of various genetic traits varies from one generation to the next because of random transference of genes. This normal occurrence is called *genetic drift*. If a population experiences a dramatic decrease in number, genetic drift occurs much faster since the number of alleles in the gene pool is small. A significant reduction in the size of a population is called a *population bottleneck*. Endangered species such as the American Bison and the black-footed ferret have suffered from genetic bottlenecks.

In this activity, you model the movement of alleles in a small gene pool, creating a population bottleneck.

Objectives

- Visualize the change in a gene pool caused by a significant decrease in the size of the population.
- Explain how a reduction of genetic variation can threaten the survival of a species.

Skills

- Practicing random sampling
- Using a model to increase understanding
- Drawing conclusions from data

Materials (per group of 2–4 students)

- beads (20 each of these colors: dark blue, light blue, orange, red, white, green, pink, purple, yellow, black)
- brown paper bag

Procedure

Preparation

The Genetic Bottleneck Data Chart at the bottom of page 88 begins with data simulating four normal, uninterrupted generations of an imaginary endangered mammal. Beads of 10 different colors are used to represent the alleles in the gene pool for that generation. Each gene codes for a certain trait. Generation 1 assumes an equal distribution of 10 beads (or alleles) in each of the 10 colors. From a well-mixed bag of 100 beads, 10 of each color, a random sample of 100 beads was drawn by drawing a bead, recording its color, replacing the bead in the bag, and then drawing the next bead. The total number of draws for each color were recorded as Generation 2. The population of Generation 2 is stable at 100 individuals, but genetic drift creates a different distribution of alleles. The bag was then reset by filling it with the numbers of beads represented by Generation 2, 100 beads total but no longer in equal numbers for each color. Another random sample of 100 beads was drawn, replacing each bead in the bag after recording its color. The total counts were recorded as Generation 3. In the same way, Generation 4 was created by a random drawing of 100 beads from Generation 3.

Modeling the Bottleneck

The population of imaginary mammals is now significantly reduced from 100 animals to 20 animals in Generation 5, thus beginning the genetic bottleneck.

1. Set up your gene pool by placing the number of beads of each color shown in the column for Generation 4 in your brown paper bag.

2. Without looking, draw a bead from the bag. Make a tally mark under Generation 5 in the row with the correct color. Replace the bead in the bag. Shake the bag and draw again. Continue to draw beads and mark the chart in this way until you have drawn 20 beads.

3. Convert your tally marks to the number of beads of each color.

4. Set up the gene pool for Generation 6 by placing the number of beads of each color shown in the column for Generation 5 in your brown paper bag.

5. Draw 20 beads for Generation 6 in the same way that you did for Generation 5, making a tally mark for each bead in the row with the correct color and replacing the bead in the bag. Convert your tally marks to numbers.

6. Set up the gene pool for Generation 7 by placing the number of beads of each color shown in the column for Generation 6 in your brown paper bag.

7. Draw 20 beads for Generation 7 in the same way that you did for Generation 6, making a tally mark for each bead in the row with the correct color and replacing the bead in the bag. Convert your tally marks to numbers.

8. Assume now that your imaginary animal population begins to recover in Generation 8. Set up the gene pool for this generation by placing the number of beads of each color shown in the column for Generation 7 in your brown paper bag.

9. Draw 40 beads for Generation 8 in the same way that you did for Generation 7, making a tally mark for each bead in the row with the correct color and replacing the bead in the bag. Convert your tally marks to numbers.

10. The Color/Trait Correspondence table below associates each bead color (allele) with a specific trait. The list includes both desirable and undesirable traits that your imaginary mammals might have inherited. Notice that alleles 7 and 8 both code for accurate hearing. Your mammal must have both alleles in order to have good hearing. Transfer the numbers for Generation 8 into the Color/Trait Correspondence table.

11. In the space below, write a paragraph that describes the general health and ability to survive of the mammals in your imaginary population.

_____

_____

_____

_____

_____

_____

_____

_____

_____

_____

_____

_____

_____

_____

#	Color	Trait	Generation 8
		Color/Trait Correspondence	
1	dark blue	visual acuity	
2	light blue	accurate sense of smell	
3	orange	healthy reproduction	
4	red	strong claws and teeth	
5	white	ability to run	
6	green	strong immune system	
7	pink	accurate hearing* *Must appear with trait 8 for your imaginary mammal to have good hearing	
8	purple	accurate hearing* *Must appear with trait 7 for your imaginary mammal to have good hearing	
9	yellow	deformity: muscle weakness	
10	black	deformity: club foot	

	Genetic Bottleneck Data Sample						
	Typical Variation			**Bottleneck**			**Rebuilding**
Trait/Color	Generation 2	Generation 3	Generation 4	Generation 5	Generation 6	Generation 7	Generation 8
Dark Blue	10	12	12				
Light Blue	8	11	16				
Orange	7	8	8				
Red	3	4	3				
White	7	7	9				
Green	14	9	4				
Pink	14	17	14				
Purple	18	15	14				
Yellow	12	9	11				
Black	7	8	9				

American bison

Water buffalo

Get ready: there is no such thing as an American buffalo, and there never has been. The animal pictured is an American bison. The American bison, as almost everyone knows, is famed for being reduced by hunting and slaughter from its prime population of 60 million during the early 19th century to an incredible low of 541 animals in 1889, a super genetic bottleneck. Since then, American bison has made a comeback and in 2016 became the national mammal of the United States.

There is also a European bison found in—yes—Europe. The only actual buffalos in the world are the various species of African buffalo, found in Africa, and the two species of water buffalo (one wild, one domestic) found all over Asia.

— **Commonplace Space** —

Appendix

Option 1: Collecting, Preserving, and Mounting Flowering Plants

Materials (per group of 2)

- shovel or trowel
- 3" × 5" cards (blank)
- measuring tape
- plant clippers or scissors
- newspaper
- masking tape

- corrugated cardboard
- magnifying glass
- garden gloves
- white posterboard, cardstock, or foamboard
- marking pen

- white tape (cloth or vinyl)
- transparent tape
- clear plastic food wrap
- field guides or internet access
- NatureID (or similar) smartphone app (optional)

Procedure

Part 1: Collecting and Pressing

Wear garden gloves as protection against thorns and possible poisonous plants. Choose a grassy location. Look for three or more different flowering plants. Using a 3" × 5" card, record as much of the following information as you can while in the field. Assign each plant a number. If you are using a smartphone app to assist with identification, image the plants in the app prior to digging them up. Collect the entire plant, including the roots. Gently shake the soil from the roots. Wrap each plant separately in folded newspaper.

Plant Identification Number _____

Common Name _____

Plant Genus _____

Height _____

Location _____

Collector/Date _____

Front of 3" × 5" card.

Describe the plant's growing habits: Does it look like grass? Does it climb? Does it form a mat on the ground with dense, low leaves? Does the stem or root ooze a milky, white fluid? Fill at least half the back of the card with descriptive information about the plant.

Back of 3" × 5" card.

When you have returned home with your plants, unwrap each specimen and observe it carefully. Complete the Descriptive Data chart in the Flowering Plants Report pages beginning on page 93. Observe the leaves, stems, roots, fruits, flowers, and seeds (if present) of each plant. Look for hairs, thorns, or spines on the leaves or stems. Examine the flowers and count the number of petals. Study the hairlike extensions on the roots. Determine whether the plants have taproots or fibrous roots. Taproots grow down into the soil with little branching. Fibrous roots spread out to form a tangled mass. Write at least one observation about each structure. Make a few sketches of parts of each plant. Refer to a field guide, the internet, or a smartphone app to determine the common names of each plant. Identify the genus. Add this information to your 3" × 5" cards and to the Report. Answer the analysis questions on the Report.

Taproot of a tamarind tree.

Fibrous roots of grass.

Construct a plant press using newspaper and corrugated cardboard. Lay a sheet of newspaper on top of a piece of cardboard. Arrange a plant so that the parts do not overlap, and the leaves and flower petals are lying flat. Place your identification card next to the plant. Lay a second sheet of newspaper over the top of the plant. Add another piece of corrugated cardboard to the stack. Continue to layer newspaper, plant, newspaper, and cardboard. Place heavy books on top the of pile to press the plants. Replace the newspaper with fresh newspaper every other day for about a week, until the plants are dry.

Part 2: Mounting

When your plants are fully pressed and dried, use them to create an attractive display. Carefully remove each plant from the press, keeping the identification card with the correct plant. Arrange each plant on a small piece of posterboard, white card stock, or foamboard. Attach the plants to the posterboard with narrow strips of cloth or vinyl tape.

On an unlined 3" × 5" card, neatly write the information shown in the example below. Copy the data from your original plant identification card, summarizing the descriptive information. Tape this card near the bottom of the posterboard on which you have taped the plant. Cover the posterboard with your mounted plants with clear, plastic food wrap. Attach the plastic wrap with transparent tape to the back of the posterboard.

Plant Identification Number	_____
Common Name	_____
Plant Genus	_____
Description	_____
	_____
	_____
Location	_____
Collector/Date	_____

Common Name: Dandelion

Plant Genus: <u>Taraxacum</u>

Description: Yellow flower on hollow stalk, fluffy
white seed head, deeply toothed
leaves clustered at base, tap root

Location: Lawn

Collector/Date: Tracy Creek / June 12, 2022

Flowering Plants Report

Summary Data

Date of collecting _____

Time spent collecting _____

Number of specimens collected _____

Descriptive Data for Each Plant

	Plant 1	Plant 2	Plant 3	Plant 4	Plant 5
Type of Plant (woody or herbaceous)					
Type of root system (taproot or fibrous)					
Basic leaf shape (broad and flat, long and narrow, needlelike, scalelike)					

Sketches

Description of Plant Structures

Record at least one important observation about each structure.

	Leaves	Stems	Roots	Fruits	Flowers	Seeds
Plant 1						
Plant 2						
Plant 3						
Plant 4						
Plant 5						

Flowering Plants Report (continued)

Plant Identification

Write the common name and genus name of each plant that you were able to identify.

Plant ID Number	Common Name	Genus
_____	_____	_____
_____	_____	_____
_____	_____	_____
_____	_____	_____
_____	_____	_____

Analysis

1. What characteristics are common among the plants you observed? What characteristics vary among the plants you observed? Sketch an example of each.

Sketches

2. Select one characteristic common among your specimens and suggest a reason why it is so.

_____

_____

_____

_____

_____

_____

3. Give the names of any insects that were present on your plants. Write a brief description of one insect and tell which plant it was on.

_____

_____

_____

_____

_____

_____

Option 2: Tree Identification Project

Materials (per group of 2)

- leaves (also flowers or fruits) from five trees
- 3" × 5" cards (blank)
- white glue
- plant clippers or scissors
- newspaper

- masking tape
- corrugated cardboard
- white posterboard, cardstock, or foamboard
- marking pen
- clear plastic food wrap

- transparent tape
- magnifying glass
- garden gloves
- field guides or internet access
- NatureID (or similar) smartphone app (optional)

Procedure

Part 1: Identifying Trees

This project will help you to learn to identify by name the common trees in your area. Trees are often identified by their leaves. Bark, flowers, and fruit are other characteristics useful for identification. If you have access to the Golden Field Guide, *Trees of North America*, begin by studying the pages entitled "How to Use this Book," "A Guide to the Families of Trees," and "Basic Features of Trees." Then take your book outside and begin to identify trees. If you know the common name of a tree, use the index to find where the tree is illustrated. Notice the range maps that show the regions where a species of tree normally grows.

Another great way to identify trees is with the optional NatureID app, or a similar smartphone app.

If you don't have access to a field guide, begin your study by searching for trees. Choose a tree to identify. Take a picture of it if you can. Make a quick sketch of the tree to capture its basic shape.

Remove several leaves from the tree. Do an internet search on "compound leaves." If the leaves you are collecting are compound, make sure you remove an entire leaf, not just a leaflet. Take samples of any flowers or fruits. Use a piece of copy paper and the side of an unwrapped crayon to make a bark rubbing, recording the texture of the bark. (To make a rubbing, place the copy paper on top of the bark and rub the side of the crayon on the paper over the bark.) Complete a 3" × 5" information card for each tree, adding information as you learn more.

Common Name	_____
Scientific Name	_____
Plant Genus	_____
Venation	_____
Location	_____
Collector/Date	_____

Venation refers to the patterns of leaf veins. The three main types of venation are parallel, pinnate, and palmate. In parallel venation, the veins are parallel to each other along the length of the leaf. In pinnate venation, the veins are in a branching pattern. One major vein down the center of the leaf has smaller veins extending outward from it. In palmate venation, two or more major veins extend outward from one point like fingers extending from the palm of a hand.

Parallel—ginkgo.

Pinnate—oak.

Palmate—maple.

Store all materials you collect from each tree separately, along with the 3" × 5" information card. Bring them home and use your app, field guide, or the internet to complete your identification of each tree. Then prepare your leaves and flowers for mounting.

Part 2: Mounting Tree Leaves

Construct a plant press using newspaper and corrugated cardboard. Lay a sheet of newspaper on top of a piece of cardboard. Arrange your leaves so the parts do not overlap, and the leaves and any flower petals are lying flat. Place your identification card next to the plant. Lay a second sheet of newspaper over the top of the plant. Add another piece of corrugated cardboard to the stack. Continue to layer newspaper, plant, newspaper, and cardboard. Place heavy books on top the of pile to press the plants. Replace the newspaper with fresh newspaper every other day for about a week, until the leaves and flowers are dry.

When your leaves are dried and pressed, plan how to arrange them on a sheet of card stock (8 ½" × 11"), posterboard, or foamboard. Print the common name of the tree at the top of each page. Include a sketch or photograph of the tree, the dried leaves and flowers (if any), a cut out from the bark rubbing you made, and your 3" × 5" information card. Use white glue to attach the items to the posterboard.

Cover the posterboard with your mounted plants with clear, plastic food wrap. Attach the plastic wrap with transparent tape to the back of the posterboard.

Green Ash

Scientific Name: <u>Fraxinus pennsylvanica</u>

Plant Genus: <u>Fraxinus</u>

Venation: Pinnate

Location: Front Yard

Collector/Date: Tracy Creek   July 1, 2022

Option 3: Insect Project

Materials (per group of 2)

- cardboard box
- cardstock
- collecting net
- fumigating jar
- glue

- insect pins
- polystyrene foam or cardboard
- magnifying glass
- scissors
- field guides or internet access

Introduction

An insect collection is a useful tool for learning how to identify and classify organisms. Insects are ubiquitous; you shouldn't have trouble finding specimens for this collection! You can search in grassy meadows, in forests, and around ponds. Look in these places:

- under stones and boards
- in rotten logs
- near lights
- on flowers, leaves, and tree bark

- on animals
- in ponds and streams
- in decaying plants and animals
- in the soil

Part 1: Equipment

Collecting insects requires a few pieces of equipment that can be either purchased or homemade. If you want to make your own equipment, here are some guidelines:

- **Collecting net.** Gather mosquito netting or nylon hosiery, a wire coat hanger, a broom handle or ¾" dowel rod, and a hose clamp. Bend the wire coat hanger into the shape of a loop that is about 12" across. Leave a straight extension of wire about 3" long at each end of the loop. Attach the straight extensions of the wire loop to the handle with a hose clamp. Hand-sew the nylon hosiery or mosquito netting to the wire loop in the shape of a bag.
- **Fumigating jar.** Obtain a glass jar such as a jelly jar or a large baby food jar. Place a layer of cotton balls in the bottom of the jar and sprinkle them with nail polish remover that contains acetone. Cut a circle of stiff cardboard that will fit snugly into the jar and place it over the cotton balls. Add more acetone to the cotton balls as needed. Be aware that acetone is flammable and that the vapors can be harmful if inhaled. Add this chemical outdoors or in a well-ventilated area.
- **Mounting Board.** A scrap of polystyrene foam packaging material or a piece of corrugated cardboard works well for a mounting board.
- **Storage Box.** Find a gift box or another cardboard box. Cut a piece of polystyrene foam to fit the bottom of the box. If you want the collection to last longer, you may attach mothballs to the corners of the polystyrene foam with insect pins.

Part 2: Collecting

A couple of useful techniques for capturing insects with a net are the swoop method and the single assault method. Use the swoop method if you are working in a grassy meadow. Walk through the meadow while swooping your net back and forth along the ground and through any vegetation. When you have collected an assortment of insects, work them into the bottom of the net. Stick the insect-filled portion of the net into your fumigating jar and close it. When the insects appear to be stunned, open the jar and empty the insects into it. Leave the insects in the jar until they are dead. The single assault method is useful for catching a butterfly or other large insect. Sneak up on the insect and quickly drop your net over it. Lift the middle of the netting bag and the captured insect will fly upward. Then trap the insect in the end of the net, place it in the fumigating jar, and close the lid. Don't attempt to chase flying insects.

Part 3: Drying and Mounting

Most of your insects can be mounted when you take them from the fumigating jar. Pin them horizontally through the thorax (the middle section of the body), leaving 3/8" of pin above each insect's body. If you have an insect that is too small to pin, cut a small triangle of paper and glue the insect to the point. Pin the paper instead of the insect. Butterflies and moths require a little more effort. After securing the insect to the mounting board, spread the wings and cover each wing with a strip of stiff paper. Pin the paper strips to the mounting board to keep the wings spread. When the insect has dried, remove the paper strips.

Part 4: Labeling and Identification

Identify each insect you collect with a small paper label giving the information shown on the example card. Study each insect carefully using a magnifying glass. Use a field guide or insect key to identify each insect by its order and common name. Use pins or glue to place each label below the pinned insect.

Common Name _____

Scientific Order _____

Place Collected _____

Collector/Date _____

A **dichotomous** key is a useful tool for categorizing insects based on their observable traits. It is made up of a series of statements with two options in each step. If your observations are accurate, a complete key will lead you to the identification of the correct order of each of your insects. The key on the following page is a short one that contains several insect orders. Use it to identify the order of as many of your insects as you can. Begin at number 1. Observe your insect to determine whether it has well-developed wings or only partial wings or no wings at all. From there you continue you to number 2 or number 12. Continue to observe your insect to determine which statement best describes it as you work your way through the key until you arrive at the order name. Use the Insect Identification Data Table on the Insect Project Report to record the key sequence you followed to arrive at the order name for each of your insects.

Dichotomous Key to Several Insect Orders

1
  a. Has well-developed wings.
          Go to number 2
  b. Has no wings or just partial wings.
          Go to number 12

2
  a. Front wings horny, leathery, or parchmentlike, at least at base. If hind wings are present, they are membranous.
          Go to number 3
  b. Wings are entirely membranous
          Go to number 6

3
  a. Mouthparts designed to function like a soda straw.
          Go to number 4
  b. Mouthparts include mandibles, used for chewing.
          Go to number 5

4
  a. Beak arises from the front of the head; front wings are usually leathery at base and membranous at tip; the tips generally overlap when at rest.
          Hemiptera (bugs)
  b. Beak arises from hind part of the head, often appearing to arise from the base of the front legs; front wings are of uniform texture throughout, the tips are not overlapped or only slightly overlapped when at rest.
          Homoptera (hoppers)

5
  a. Front wings are without veins, and usually meet in a straight line down the middle of the back; antennae generally have 11 or fewer segments; hind wings narrow, are usually longer than the front wings when unfolded, and have few veins.
          Coleoptera (beetles)
  b. Front wings have veins and are either held roof-like over abdomen or overlap over abdomen when at rest; antennae generally have more than 12 segments; hind wings broad, usually shorter than front wings, and have many veins.
          Orthoptera (grasshoppers, crickets, cockroaches)

6
  a. Has two wings.
          Go to number 7
  b. Has four wings.
          Go to number 8

7
  a. Body grasshopper-like with hind legs enlarged.
          Orthoptera (pygmy grasshoppers)
  b. Body not grasshopper-like. Has sucking mouthparts. Tarsus of leg nearly always has 5 segments
          Diptera (true flies)

8
  a. Wings largely or entirely covered with scales; mouthparts usually form a coiled proboscis; antennae have many segments.
          Lepidoptera (butterflies and moths)
  b. Wings not covered by scales and proboscis not coiled.
          Go to number 9

9
  a. Tarsus (final major part of the leg) has 5 segments.
          Go to number 10
  b. Tarsus has 4 or fewer segments.
          Go to number 11

10
  a. Rather hard-bodied, wasplike insects, the abdomen often constricted at base; hind wings smaller than front wings and with fewer veins.
          Hymenoptera (wasps and bees)
  b. Mouthparts for chewing, not being in the form of a tube.
          Go to number 11

11
  a. Hind wings as long as the front wings and of the same shape or wider at the base; wings usually held outstretched; abdomen long; slender tarsi have 3 segments.
          Odonata (dragonflies, damselflies)
  b. Beak arising from hind part of the head.
          Homoptera (cicadas, aphids)

12
  a. Abdomen constricted at base, antennae usually elbowed; hard-bodied, antlike insects.
          Hymenoptera (ants)
  b. Beak arising from front part of head; antennae usually have 4 or 5 segments; tarsi usually have 3 segments.
          Hemiptera (wingless bugs)

Insect Report

Data

Date of collecting _____

Time spent collecting _____

Number of specimens collected _____

Number of different kinds of insects collected _____

Season of the year_____

Type of living area_____

Time of day you collected_____

Weather conditions _____

Insect Identification

Insect #	Key Sequence	Order
1		
2		
3		
4		
5		
6		
7		
8		
9		
10		
11		
12		
13		
14		
15		

Analysis

1. Name and describe some insects you collected with which you are familiar.

_____

_____

_____

2. Describe an insect you found that you have never seen before.

_____

_____

_____

_____

3. Sketch the largest insect you found and describe its activities.

_____

_____

_____

_____

_____

_____

_____

_____

_____

_____

_____

┌─── Sketches ───┐

4. Sketch the most unusual insect you found and describe its activities.

_____

_____

_____

_____

_____

_____

_____

_____

_____

_____

_____

_____

┌─── Sketches ───┐

5. Which insects seemed to be the most numerous?

_____

_____

_____

_____

6. Which insects seemed to be the scarcest?

_____

_____

_____

_____

_____

7. List common characteristics in several of your insects.

_____

_____

_____

_____

8. Describe an insect with unique characteristics.

_____

_____

_____

_____

References and Image Credits

4. AdobeStock_154816785.ai. Author: OneLineStock.com, used under license. 4. AdobeStock_510202617. ai. Author: dhtgstockphoto, used under license. 6. image: Date_Seed_sprouting-002.jpg via https:// commons.wikimedia.org/wiki/File:Date_Seed_sprouting-002.jpg. Author: Amada44, public domain. 6. quote: Henry Thoreau, *Faith in a Seed: The Dispersion of Seeds and Other Late Natural History Writings*, Island Press, p. xvii. 10. New Shoots Poetry Anthology, p. 37; used by permission. 13. top/bottom. John D. Mays (photograph of the inscription on the tower at the University of Texas at Austin). 13. image: Mark_ Twain_Sarony.jpeg via https://commons.wikimedia.org/wiki/File:Mark_Twain_Sarony.jpg. Author: Napoleon Sarony, public domain. 13. quote: see https://www.barrypopik.com/index.php/new_york_city/ entry/if_you_tell_the_truth/. 15. image: AdobeStock_508891798.jpeg. Author: Marina, used under license. 15. poem: *Christina Rossetti, The Complete Poems*, Penguin Classics, p. 245. 17. image: AdobeStock_90859817.jpeg. Author: tomeyk, used under license. 17. Sam Kean quote: *The Disappearing Spoon*, Sam Kean, Back Bay Books, p. 168. 17. historical note source: https://www.science.org/content/ article/ancient-native-americans-were-among-world-s-first-coppersmiths. 17. Flight_of_Lot.png via https:// commons.wikimedia.org/wiki/File:Flight_of_Lot.png. Author: Gustave Doré, public domain. 22. prokaryotic cell: adapted from OSC_Microbio_03_03_PartsProk_img.jpg via https://commons.wikimedia. org/wiki/File:OSC_Microbio_03_03_PartsProk_img.jpg. Author: CNX OpenStax, licensed under CC-BY-SA 4.0. 23. adapted from OSC_Microbio_03_04_eukcell.jpg via https://commons.wikimedia.org/wiki/ File:OSC_Microbio_03_04_eukcell.jpg. Author: CNX OpenStax, licensed under CC-BY-SA 4.0. 23. adapted from Figure 04 03 01b.png via https://commons.wikimedia.org/wiki/File:Figure_04_03_01b.png. Author: CNX OpenStax, licensed under CC-BY-SA 4.0. 23. Robert Hooke, *Micrographia*, p. 116, accessed through Google Books. 26. Blausen_0229_ClassificationofBones.png via https://commons.wikimedia.org/ wiki/File:Blausen_0229_ClassificationofBones.png. Author: BruceBlaus, licensed under CC-BY-SA 3.0. 26. From *The Collected Poems of William Carlos Williams*, *Volume I*, A. Walton Litz & Christopher MacGowan, eds., p. 224. 29. From *The Loves of Pelleas and Etarre*, p. 33. 31. John D. Mays. 32. Onion_root_mitosis. jpeg via https://commons.wikimedia.org/wiki/File:Onion_root_mitosis.jpg. Author: staticd, licensed under CC-BY-SA 3.0. 33. AdobeStock_235486805.jpeg. Author: Alexmar, used under license. 33. quote: https:// dartreview.com/some-thoughts-from-robert-frost/. 35. lllustration_Apium_graveolens0.jpeg via https:// commons.wikimedia.org/wiki/File:Illustration_Apium_graveolens0.jpg. Author: Prof. Dr. Otto Wilhelm Thomé Flora von Deutschland, Österreich und der Schweiz 1885, Gera, Germany, public domain. 35. AdobeStock_80033744.jpeg. Author: niteenrk, used under license. 37. From *Thomas Hardy: The Complete Poems*, p. 434. 37. AdobeStock_417343694.jpeg. Author: fizkes, used under license. 39. I_vapor.png via https://commons.wikimedia.org/wiki/File:I_vapor.png. Author: 2x910, licensed under CC-BY-SA 4.0. 40. Yeast: S_cerevisiae_under_DIC_microscopy.jpeg via https://commons.wikimedia.org/wiki/File:S_ cerevisiae_under_DIC_microscopy.jpg. Author: Masur, public domain. 41. John D. Mays. 43. AdobeStock_122059917.jpeg. Author: jarun011, used under license. 43. poem: John D. Mays. 49. AdobeStock_78358694.jpeg. Author: WavebreakMediaMicro, used under license. 49. From Hugh Lofting, *The Story of Doctor Doolittle*, 1948, p. 148. 49. source for item on human smell: https://www.nih.gov/ news-events/nih-research-matters/humans-can-identify-more-1-trillion-smells. 52. AdobeStock_535338363. ai. Author: Anna Sokol, used under license. 52. AdobeStock_164246586.jpeg. Author: Naj, used under license. 52. From *Robert Frost: The Road not Taken: An Introduction to his Poetry*, Louis Untermeyer, ed., p. 5, 6. 54. Wheat_and_chessboard_problem.jpeg via https://commons.wikimedia.org/wiki/File:Wheat_and_ chessboard_problem.jpg. Author: McGeddon, licensed under CC-BY-SA 4.0. 57. flower: FibonacciChamomile.png via https://commons.wikimedia.org/wiki/File:FibonacciChamomile.PNG. Author: RDBury, licensed under CC-BY-SA 2.5. 57. bee: Honigbiene(Apis_mellifera).svg via https:// commons.wikimedia.org/wiki/File:Honigbiene(Apis_mellifera).svg. Author: birdy geimfyglið (:>)=|, public domain. 60. mosquito: Aedes_aegypti_biting_human.jpeg via https://commons.wikimedia.org/wiki/ File:Aedes_aegypti_biting_human.jpg. Author: US Department of Agriculture, public domain. 60. source

of malaria article: https://www.nature.com/articles/news021001-6. refuting the half of all deaths claim: https://ourworldindata.org/malaria-introduction. (see also footnote 7). 61. AdobeStock_371250076.jpeg. Author: slowmotiongli, used under license. 61. AdobeStock_29201076.jpeg. Author: define, used under license. 61. AdobeStock_7705806.jpeg. Author: Mary Durden, used under license. 61. AdobeStock_228691561.jpeg. Author: andreanita, used under license. 61. AdobeStock_326690259.jpeg. Author: J Esteban Berrio, used under license. 61. AdobeStock_146600211.jpeg. Author: volkan, used under license. 63. The_leggiest_animal_on_the_planet,_Eumillipes_persephone,_from_Australia—female_individual_with_1,306_legs.jpeg via https://en.wikipedia.org/wiki/File:The_leggiest_animal_on_the_planet,_Eumillipes_persephone,_from_Australia%E2%80%94female_individual_with_1,306_legs.jpg. Author: Aggyrolemnoixytes/Paul Marek, licensed under CC-BY-SA 4.0. 67. AdobeStock_278441176.jpeg. Author: LUGOSTOCK, used under license. 67. poem: From *W.B. Yeats, The Poems, Volume I*, Richard J. Finneran, ed., p. 131. 69. AdobeStock_175727818.jpeg. Author: Sergej Ljashenko, used under license. 69. quote: From John Muir, *My First Summer in the Sierra*, in *Muir, Nature Writings*, Library of America, p. 191. 72. image: AdobeStock_43312716.jpeg. Author: livingstonphoto, used under license. 72. quote: From John Steinbeck, *The Log from the Sea of Cortez*, in *Steinbeck, The Grapes of Wrath and other Writings, 1936–1941*, Library of America, p. 929. 75. portrait: Arthur-Tansley-1893.jpeg via https://commons.wikimedia.org/wiki/File:Arthur-Tansley-1893.jpg. Author: anonymous, public domain. 75. image: AdobeStock_139961371.jpeg. Author: Doug, used under license. 75. quote: Ralph Waldo Emerson, *Nature*, Thurston, Torry, and Co., 1849, p. 11. 78. Andes_Mountains_-_Chile_-_Sarah_Stierch.jpeg via https://commons.wikimedia.org/wiki/File:Andes_Mountains_-_Chile_-_Sarah_Stierch.jpg. Author: Sarah Stierch, licensed under CC-BY-SA 4.0. 79. Appalachian_Mountains_wallpaper.jpeg via https://commons.wikimedia.org/wiki/File:Appalachian_Mountains_wallpaper.jpg. Author: MrSparkle17, licensed under CC-BY-SA 4.0. 79. Mount_Everest_as_seen_from_Drukair2_PLW_edit.jpeg via https://commons.wikimedia.org/wiki/File:Mount_Everest_as_seen_from_Drukair2_PLW_edit.jpg. Author: shrimpo1967, revised by Papa Lima Whiskey 2, licensed under CC-BY-SA 2.0. 80. Mini_Alluvial_Fan_Imprinted_with_Footprints.jpeg via https://commons.wikimedia.org/wiki/File:Mini_Alluvial_Fan_Imprinted_with_Footprints.jpg. Author: Wing-Chi Poon, licensed under CC-BY-SA 2.5. 81. Gfp-missouri-taum-sauk-mountain-state-park-ozark-mountains.jpeg via https://commons.wikimedia.org/wiki/File:Gfp-missouri-taum-sauk-mountain-state-park-ozark-mountains.jpg. Author: Yinan Chen, public domain. 81. Great_view_over_the_swiss_alps_(Unsplash).jpeg via https://commons.wikimedia.org/wiki/File:Great_view_over_the_swiss_alps_(Unsplash).jpg. Author: René Reichelt, public domain. 81. Rocky_Mountain_National_Park_in_September_2011_-_Glacier_Gorge_from_Bear_Lake.jpeg via https://commons.wikimedia.org/wiki/File:Rocky_Mountain_National_Park_in_September_2011_-_Glacier_Gorge_from_Bear_Lake.JPG. Author: Daniel Mayer (Mav), licensed under CC-BY-SA 3.0. 81. poem: From "The Flowing", in Gary Snyder, *Mountains and Rivers Without End*, p. 70. 84. AdobeStock_62786758.jpeg. Author: logos2012, used under license. 89. American_bison_k5680-1.jpeg via https://commons.wikimedia.org/wiki/File:American_bison_k5680-1_edit.jpg. Author: Jack Dykinga, Agricultural Research Service, public domain. 89. Water_Buffalo_at_Wilpattu_National_Park.jpeg via https://commons.wikimedia.org/wiki/File:Water_Buffalo_at_Wilpattu_National_Park.jpg. Author: Manelka Jayasundara, licensed under CC-BY-SA 4.0. 91. Starr-070404-6562-Leucaena_leucocephala-taproot_profile_in_roadcut-Keomoku_Rd-Lanai_(24258711924).jpeg via https://commons.wikimedia.org/wiki/File:Starr-070404-6562-Leucaena_leucocephala-taproot_profile_in_roadcut-Keomoku_Rd-Lanai_(24258711924).jpg. Author: Forest and Kim Starr, licensed under CC-BY-SA 3.0. 91. 2011-03-22_Poa-annua-roots.jpeg via https://commons.wikimedia.org/wiki/File:2011-03-22_Poa-annua-roots.JPG. Author: Sten Porse, licensed under CC-BY-SA 3.0. 91. Leontodon_autumnalis_herbarium_sample.jpeg via https://commons.wikimedia.org/wiki/File:Leontodon_autumnalis_herbarium_sample.jpg. Author: Sunk3rn, public domain. 92. Tracy Creek. 98. Gingko_biloba_branch.jpeg via https://commons.wikimedia.org/wiki/File:Gingko_biloba_branch.jpg. Author: Júlio Reis, licensed under CC-BY-SA 2.5. 98. Leaf_veins_oak.jpeg via https://commons.wikimedia.org/wiki/File:Leaf_veins_oak.jpg. Author: Dvortygirl, licensed under